STANDING ROOM ONLY

Karl Sax, professor of botany at Harvard, is on the staff of the Bussey Institution (formerly Harvard's school of agriculture). He has published more than a hundred papers in the fields of genetics, cytology, horticulture, and demography. His articles on demographic subjects have appeared in *Science, Scientific Monthly, United Nations World,* and the *Proceedings of the American Academy of Arts and Sciences;* and he contributed chapters to *The Science of Man* (1945) and to *Twentieth Century Economic Thought* (1949).

Standing Room Only

THE WORLD'S EXPLODING POPULATION

by

Karl Sax

NEW EDITION

BEACON PRESS   BOSTON

Some of the material in this book was first presented in a series of
lectures given in Boston in 1951, under the sponsorship of the Lowell
Institute.

Library of Congress catalog card number: 55-7799
Printed in U.S.A.

20672

Contents

PREFACE ix

INTRODUCTION 3

I. THE HUMAN FACTOR

1. The Malthusian Laws 11
2. The Growth of the Human Population 28
3. The Demographic Transition 42

II. THE MATERIAL RESOURCES

4. Food for the World 63
5. Energy and Minerals: Consumption and Reserves 87
6. The New Frontiers of Science 104

III. PROSPECTS FOR THE FUTURE

7. Two-thirds of the World 127
8. Escape from Poverty 147
9. The Obstacles of Tradition 158
10. The Conflict Between Creeds and Needs 176

BIBLIOGRAPHY 193

INDEX 202

Figures and Tables

The Population Problem   viii

Figure 1. " Positive Checks " or " Preventive Checks "?   19
Figure 2. The Geography of Hunger   25
Figure 3. World Population Growth (5000 B.C. to 1950 A.D.)   35
Figure 4. Potential Population Growth   37
Figure 5. The Demographic Transition in England   55
Figure 6. Emigration and the Demographic Transition   59
Figure 7. World Production of Bread Grains   71
Figure 8. The Arable Land of the World   81
Figure 9. The Uses of Solar Energy   117
Figure 10. The Challenge of Overpopulation   177

Table 1. Demographic Status of the World   24
Table 2. World Population (1650–1950)   28
Table 3. Estimates of the World's Arable Land   73
Table 4. The World's Distribution of Land and People   80
Table 5. Source and Use of Energy Per Capita   88
Table 6. The World's Coal Resources   92
Table 7. The World's Water-Power Resources   97
Table 8. The World's Mineral Resources   100
Table 9. U.S. Dependence on Foreign Sources of Minerals   101
Table 10. Economic and Cultural Status of the World   128
Table 11. Raushenbush's Projection of Trends   156
Table 12. Animal-Protein Consumption and Birth Rates   165
Table 13. Birth Rates in Catholic and Non-Catholic Areas   185

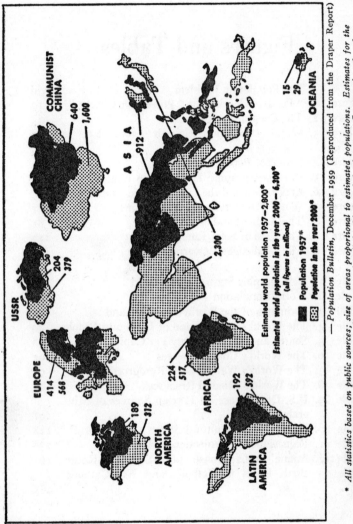

COMMUNIST CHINA 640 1,600

USSR 204 379

ASIA 912 2,300

EUROPE 414 568

AFRICA 224 517

NORTH AMERICA 189 312

LATIN AMERICA 192 592

OCEANIA 15 29

Estimated world population 1957—2,800*
Estimated world population in the year 2000 — 6,300*
(all figures in millions)

■ Population 1957*
▨ Population in the year 2000*

— *Population Bulletin*, December 1959 (Reproduced from the Draper Report)

* All statistics based on public sources; size of areas proportional to estimated populations. Estimates for the year 2000 based on United Nations "medium assumptions" for birth and death rates. Computations based on the U. N. projections result in estimated average rates of annual population increase per area as follows: Europe, 0.7%; North America, 1.2%; USSR, 1.4%; Oceania, 1.4%; Africa, 1.8%; Communist China, 2.1%; Asia, 2.1%; Latin America, 2.7%.

Preface to the New Edition

The first edition of *Standing Room Only* called attention to the race between population growth and the expansion of resources, based largely upon the situation existing in 1950. During the past decade, the world population has grown at an unprecedented rate. The increasing rate of population growth has been so acute that many responsible people now acknowledge the " population explosion " as the greatest threat to world peace and prosperity. In the words of Harry Emerson Fosdick: " The population question is the basic problem of the world today, and unless we can solve it . . . , no other major problem of our world society can be solved at all."

In 1950 the world population was estimated at little more than 2.4 billion; it was growing at a rate of little more than 1 per cent annually. By 1960 the world population exceeded 2.8 billion and was growing at an annual rate of nearly 2 per cent. Predictions were made, early in this past decade, that the world population might reach 4 billion by the year 2000. In 1958 the United Nations Department of Economic and Social Affairs predicted an increase 50 per cent higher — a world population of more than 6 billion by the end of this century. And the present world rate of growth is far from the maximum. In many countries, populations are growing at the annual rate of

3 per cent or more — a rate that would double the population in less than 25 years. For all of Latin America, the rate is 2.5 per cent.

The most tragic aspect of the population explosion is that the greatest rate of growth is in Asia, Africa, and Latin America, where most of the people are already living at or near bare subsistence levels, with inadequate food, housing, education, and medical care. Even in the underdeveloped countries which have adequate potential resources, excessive population growth is swamping agricultural and economic development. Many Latin American countries have adequate land and other resources to support larger populations; but Harrison Brown predicts that nearly all of Latin America is likely to be, for the next 100 years, one vast urban and rural slum. Asia, with far less adequate per capita resources, faces an even more dismal future in supporting its 4 billion inhabitants expected by the end of this century.

In the race between the population explosion and the development of the world's resources, encouraging advances have been made. Sources of energy have been developed which can probably meet all needs in the foreseeable future. Although the problem of harnessing nuclear fusion is not yet solved, progress has been made in developing breeder reactors that should provide ample atomic energy. Alvin Weinberg has predicted (in *Scientific American*, January 1960) that even at 20 times the present energy consumption, the reservoir of energy available in either the rocks or the sea would last for 10 billion years. But, as the Political and Economic Planning commission of England warned in 1955, " the importance to mankind of nuclear power lies not in the present nor in the near future, but in the distant future." At the present rate of growth, the world population will soon reach 10 billion. If, at that time, the per capita use of energy is to equal that of the United States today, the production of energy would have to be increased 40-fold during the next 70 years. The need is urgent, and the time is short.

The need for more food is the most urgent problem facing the world today. More than half of the world's people do not get enough to eat. Hunger is an old story in human history. It is reflected in the Lord's Prayer, where the appeal for food takes priority over the appeal for forgiveness of sins. The same philosophy is expressed in the ancient Chinese proverb, " It is difficult to tell the difference between right and wrong when the stomach is empty." The wisdom of the Chinese is also reflected in their word for peace, *ho-ping*, which means literally " food for all." In more recent times, Gandhi observed that " to the millions who have to go without two meals a day, the only acceptable form in which God dare appear is food."

In most of the underdeveloped countries, food production is barely keeping pace with population growth. It should be possible to double food production by orthodox agricultural techniques; but it will take time, and time is limited. At present rates of growth the population of Latin America, Africa, and Asia will be doubled in 30 to 35 years. Eventually agriculture should be able to provide ample food of good quality for 5 billion people and a subsistence diet for 10 billion. But if the rate of food production does not exceed the rate of population growth, the only result will be more people living in poverty.

At the Rothamstead Station in England, techniques and machines have been devised to extract proteins from grass and other foliage. This is far more efficient than feeding grass and grain to animals so as to have protein in the form of milk, meat, and eggs, though it is not very exciting from a gastronomic point of view. Some progress has also been made in culturing algae for food; but in no country has this promising but expensive technique been put into commercial operation.

With the unlimited energy resources now in prospect, it is theoretically possible to de-salt enough sea water to irrigate the deserts of the world; to build plastic domes over farmland and provide artificial heat and light, so that crops could be grown in the arctic; to construct underground caverns where light and temperature control would permit hydroponic agriculture anywhere in the world; to grow algae on spaceships; and eventually, perhaps, to dispense with plants and produce food by artificial photosynthesis. These techniques might permit a world population of hundreds of billions. The cost would, of course, be staggering, but time is a still more critical factor. At the present rate of growth, the world population would reach 100 billion in less than 200 years — and more than 3000 billion in less than 500 years.

In short, while great advances are possible in food production and industry, even the most fantastic increases cannot possibly keep pace with the present rate of population growth for any significant period of time. In 600 years the entire earth would provide only one square yard of land per person; long before that time, we would have to grow algae in spaceships to provide our food. In about

1700 years, unless there were migration to other planets, the weight of humanity would exceed the weight of the earth.

Migration to other planets, as an alternative to birth control, has recently been suggested by the Director of the Family Life Bureau of the National Catholic Welfare Conference. The feasibility of such migration has been considered by Garrett Hardin, who points out (in *Journal of Heredity*, March–April 1959) that the nearest star is Alpha Centauri, 4.3 light years away. Even at an average speed of 7 million miles per hour, a rocket ship would take 350 years to reach the nearest planet outside our own solar system.

Assuming that the world could support a population of 10 billion and that population growth continues at the present rate, in 70 years it would be necessary to move 170 million people each year. Assuming 100 passengers per spaceship, the migration would require 1.7 million spaceships each year — at a cost, Hardin estimates, of $300 million per ship. But if birth control is not to be practiced on earth, it would surely not be practiced on the spaceships. If only one couple started the trip, the number of progeny (even allowing for the deleterious effects of inbreeding) would be about 2000 at the end of the trip. Thus it would be necessary to provide 85 million spaceships every year, each with a capacity of 2000 and at a cost of several billion dollars or more per ship.

But even such mass migration would afford only temporary relief, for if the migrants to other planets continued to increase at present rates, the mass of humanity would exceed the weight of the entire universe in about 6000 years, and the area they occupy would be expanding with the speed of light.

It is obvious that the present rate of world population growth cannot be maintained for any significant period of time. Either death rates must increase, or birth rates must be decreased. During recent years, great progress has been made in developing birth control techniques. The oral contraceptive has been perfected by Gregory Pincus of the Worcester Foundation in Massachusetts and John Rock, professor emeritus of the Harvard Medical School. Their steroid pill acts like the hormone of pregnancy, preventing ovulation. Taken once a day for 20 days after menstruation, it is nearly 100 per cent effective. But the cost is prohibitive, and further tests are needed to check for undesired side effects. Warren Nelson of the Rockefeller Institute is confident, however, that adequate research could produce an effective, foolproof, safe, and inexpensive contraceptive in from 5 to 10 years.

If the time of ovulation could be determined precisely, the Rhythm method of birth control, permitted by the Catholic Church, would be much more reliable. The tests now available have proved to be unsatisfactory, but perhaps a hormone pill could be used to induce ovulation at a precise period during the menstrual cycle. Yet neither this method nor the contraceptives commonly used would be of much value among the illiterate masses of the underdeveloped countries.

Perhaps the greatest obstacle to a rational approach to the population problem has been the conspiracy of silence. During the past year, however, the conspiracy has been broken: the press, radio, and television have featured statements by leaders in religion, public health, and government.

A study group of the World Council of Churches at Oxford University in April 1959, considering " Responsible Parenthood and the Population Problem," concluded that " where there is grinding poverty, a high birth rate, high death rate and high infant mortality, a fatalistic attitude to death is almost inevitable, and a high valuation of human personality is difficult to attain." It recommended that the wealthier nations with low birth rates help the people of underdeveloped lands to exercise responsible parenthood.

In July 1959, the President's Committee to Study the U.S. Military Assistance Program transmitted its report to the President, who transmitted it to Congress. The committee, headed by William H. Draper, observed that " the increase in food production in most of the underdeveloped countries has been falling behind the increase in population. . . . Unless the relationship between the present trends of population growth and food production is reversed, the already difficult task of economic development will become a practical impossibility." The Draper Report recommended that the United States assist these countries, when asked to do so, with plans to deal with the problem of rapid population growth and that it support research for ways to meet the serious problems resulting from the population explosion.

In September 1959, the U.S. Senate Foreign Affairs Committee, headed by Senator J. William Fulbright, asked the Stanford Research Institute to study certain aspects

of U.S. foreign aid policies. The Stanford group observed
that "in a finite world some means of controlling population growth are inescapable. The traditional means have
been disease, famine and war. If other means are to be
substituted, conscious national and international policies
will be required." They suggested more research to provide a safe, effective, and inexpensive oral contraceptive.

In October 1959, the Governing Council of the American Public Health Association concluded that "no problem — whether it be housing, education, food supply, recreation, communication, medical care — can be effectively
solved today if tomorrow's population increases out of
proportion to those resources available to meet those problems. . . . The public health profession has long taken
leadership in defeating disease, disability and death. It
must now assume equal leadership in understanding public
health implications of population imbalance and in taking
appropriate action."

This rational conclusion met with vigorous opposition
from the Catholic Bishops of the United States. At their
annual meeting in November 1959, they declared: "United States Catholics believe that the promotion of artificial
birth prevention is a morally, humanly, psychologically
and politically disastrous approach to the population problem." (Yet, as is shown in subsequent chapters, all available evidence indicates that the majority of Catholics in
Europe and the United States practice contraception.)
The Bishops recognized the existence of population problems, but asserted that Catholics "will not . . . support any public assistance, either at home or abroad, to
promote artificial birth prevention, abortion or steriliza-

tion whether through direct aid or by means of international organizations."

The statement by the Catholic Bishops inevitably made birth control a political as well as a religious issue. It is not surprising that politicians took cover or resorted to political expediency. Alonzo Smith, press officer of the U.S. Department of State, announced that " not one penny of foreign aid funds has ever been used for dissemination of birth control information, and there are no plans to do so." President Eisenhower assured the press that " this Government has not and will not . . . , as long as I am here, have a positive political doctrine in its program that has to do with this problem of birth control. That's not our business."

The irrational attitude of the Catholic Church regarding birth control has not changed. (It is dealt with in this book — and more fully in Alvah Sulloway's *Birth Control and Catholic Doctrine*.) Surely no intelligent Catholic approves of the Very Rev. Francis J. Connell's thesis (*see page 180*) that an overpopulated country may properly wage an aggressive war to solve its population problem. In the atomic age, such a suggestion borders on insanity.

The Communists have also maintained their opposition to birth control — even in China, where population pressure is severe. For several years the Chinese supported a birth control program, but they have now accepted the Communist party line. The editor of the *Peiping Review Journal* assured his readers on August 3, 1958, that " the larger the population, even greater will be the amount of grain produced. So long as we have the need, we can produce as much grain as we want." He then attacked the Malthusian doctrine as "a reactionary, inhuman theory."

The solution of the world's population problems is made much more difficult by this Catholic and Communist opposition to any effective method of birth control. It would be tragic if primitive religious taboos, irrational political dogma, biological illiteracy, and political expediency should conspire to prevent or delay a rational solution of the problem. The Malthusian laws of population growth are as valid today as when they were formulated 162 years ago. Population growth must be controlled, either by high death rates or by low birth rates. The world must soon choose whether future population growth is to be controlled by enlightened and artificial birth control or by the ancient destroyers — pestilence, famine, and war.

Karl Sax

NEW HAVEN, CONNECTICUT
JANUARY 1960

STANDING ROOM ONLY

Introduction

Promises of an abundant life, of freedom from want, for all mankind are usually made with little or no consideration of the population problem. The progress of the Western nations during the past century has shown that poverty and high death rates are not inevitable. The people of both the modern industrial nations and the economically underdeveloped countries of the world are now aware of the possibilities of human advancement; but few are aware of the problems and difficulties which must be solved if all of the world's people are to escape from hunger and poverty.

An official United States publication, *The United Nations' Fight for the Four Freedoms*, optimistically states: "Beyond any doubt, men possess the technical ability to produce in great abundance the necessities of daily life — enough for everyone." Kirtley Mather, past president of the American Association for the Advancement of Science, assures us that there are not only abundant resources for all of the world's people, but "enough and to spare" (70).*

It is true that we have the knowledge, the techniques, and the resources to increase the agricultural and indus-

* NOTE: Throughout the text, numbers in parentheses refer to the Bibliography (pages 193–201).

trial production of the world as a whole — though the development of the necessary education, capital, technical skills, and responsible governments will be a difficult task. But the problem of population growth is a much greater obstacle to world rehabilitation than problems of agricultural, industrial, and educational development.

In spite of war, hunger, and epidemics, the world population has increased about fourfold during the past three hundred years. At present the human population is growing at the rate of more than 1 per cent per year, a rate which doubles the population in less than 70 years. The world must now provide for an additional 30 million people every year. Every decade the resources of the world must provide for an added population equal to that of all of North and South America.

The problem is made much more difficult by the fact that the greatest growth, or potential growth, is in the underdeveloped areas of the world, where population pressure is already acute and living standards are low. These areas, with nearly two-thirds of the world's people, still have to make the "Demographic Transition" — the transition from a high-birth-rate, high-death-rate culture (with low living standards) to a low-birth-rate, low-death-rate culture (with relatively high living standards).

When the populations of the modern Western nations made this transition (beginning about 1800), they increased approximately threefold in numbers. If low birth rates must await educational and economic developments, it is very improbable that any nation under the most favorable conditions could make the Demographic Transition without at least a threefold increase in population.

Rapid population growth during this transition is the most difficult problem in world rehabilitation.

The basic biological factor in the recent unprecedented growth of the human population is the reduction of the death rate without a corresponding reduction in the birth rate. Primitive man had to have a high birth rate to compensate for a high death rate. Modern man has reduced death rates in many countries to about a third of that of his primitive ancestors; but there is no evidence of any significant decline in modern man's inherent fertility. He has reduced his fecundity by various means, but the delay in reducing birth rates has led to explosive population growth.

Although the problems of population pressure were recognized by earlier writers, it was not until almost 1800 that the laws of population growth were definitely formulated by Thomas Robert Malthus. Despite numerous attempts by clerics, political leaders, and even scientists to discredit Malthus, the essential principles of his laws of population growth are as valid today as they were 150 years ago. Populations tend to grow faster than the means of subsistence; therefore they must be controlled either by " positive checks," which increase the death rate, or by "preventive checks," which reduce the birth rate. The utmost development of agriculture and industry cannot possibly keep pace with a population growth arising from a *natural* birth rate and a *modern* death rate.

In dealing with problems of the Demographic Transition, it is necessary to consider many factors — human reproduction, agriculture, industrialization, economics, political philosophy, and religious dogma. The controversial nature of many of these subjects is perhaps the reason why population problems are so seldom studied by private foundations, government agencies, or international organizations devoted to the rehabilitation of the more backward areas of the world. Perhaps, however, the reluctance to face the population problem stems from a more fundamental inhibition, based upon primitive instincts — instincts which were essential for the survival of early man, but which are now a threat to our modern civilization.

In the following chapters the factors that have led to the recent unprecedented growth of the world's population are considered in relation to agriculture, industry, and medicine. Recent advances in science have greatly increased the means of subsistence, but they have not invalidated the inexorable laws of population growth. Continued advances in science and the exploitation of the world's natural resources may permit rapid growth of populations in much of the world for many years; but relatively soon all population growth must be controlled either by high death rates or by low birth rates.

Only the people of the modern Western nations have adopted the " preventive checks " in the control of population growth. In completing the Demographic Transition, the people of Western Europe, of North America, and of Oceania (Australia and New Zealand) have had ample resources of stored energy, arable land, and minerals. Comparable resources are not now available to most of the peoples of Asia, Africa, and Latin America, who still live little above subsistence levels.

A modern industrial civilization demands enormous

quantities of energy and minerals. The highly industrialized countries are rapidly depleting their reserves of energy and some of their critical minerals and metals.
Many nations are now drawing heavily on the resources
of the industrially undeveloped countries. Unless the
new frontiers of science can develop abundant new sources
of energy and essential minerals, our industrial culture
will be but a brief episode in human history.

Any adequate program for world rehabilitation must
include a consideration of all the problems and possibilities. In many areas poverty exists because the natural
resources are undeveloped. Some countries maintain
high living standards by exploiting their resources with
no thought of future generations. Science has made great
contributions to agriculture, industry, and medicine and
will doubtless make even greater contributions in the future. But the laws of population growth cannot be ignored.

If the adoption of " preventive checks " to population
growth in the underdeveloped areas of the world must
await a relatively high level of economic and educational
development — as it has in the modern Western nations
— it will be impossible for all of the world's people to effect the Demographic Transition. If birth rates cannot
be reduced during the early phases of the development,
all increase in the production of agriculture and industry
will be absorbed by rapid population growth, and the only
result will be more people living at subsistence levels.

The failure of religious and political leaders to face
these facts is the greatest obstacle to world rehabilitation.
Catholic spokesmen insist that " birth control is against

God's law " and comparable to murder. Meanwhile Communist leaders in Russia refer to birth control as a " cannibalistic theory " and maintain: " The more people we have, the stronger our country will be."

Yet there can be no hope for a decent life for all mankind unless birth rates in all parts of the world are soon reduced to little more than a third of man's natural birth rate.

PART ONE

THE HUMAN FACTOR

1

The Malthusian Laws

More than a century and a half ago the English clergyman and social economist Malthus first formulated his general laws of population growth. His basic premise was that populations of all species of plants and animals, including man, tend to increase faster than the means of subsistence. Population growth must, therefore, be controlled either by checking the rate of reproduction or by maintaining high death rates.

Although Malthus realized that varying capacities for food production in different areas would permit a varying growth of human populations, he maintained that populations tend to increase by geometrical progression, while food supplies increase more nearly by arithmetical progression. If, for example, the population in a given area was doubling every twenty-five years, the increase would be in the order of 1-2-4-8-16, so that in a hundred years the population would increase sixteenfold. But the food supply might increase in the order of 1-2-3-4-5, so that at the end of a hundred years the food per capita would be only a third of what the initial population had had.

Such a general formula was necessarily inexact; but it enabled Malthus to predict that when the population of England reached 44 million the island's agriculture would

feed only 33 million. England today, with a population
of 50 million, must import at least 50 per cent of her
food in order to maintain an adequate but austere diet
for her people.

Since the first publication of *An Essay on the Principle
of Population* in 1798, the Malthusian doctrine has been
attacked and criticized. Religious and political leaders
opposed it because it postulated controls of population
growth; a limited population could not provide the
hordes of faithful parishioners and the large armies necessary for the proper glorification of God and Country.
Friends of labor — with some justification — considered
Malthus a spokesman for the aristocracy. Poverty, he
contended, seemed to be inevitable and therefore justified.
The Prime Minister, William Pitt, who had earlier believed that every man who fathered many children " enriched his country," changed his views after reading Malthus' *Essay on Population* — and withdrew his Poor Bill
of 1800. Malthus himself had little faith in " prudential
restraint " as a method of controlling birth rates, and he
did not approve of contraception.

With the expanding frontiers of the New World and
the great development of industry and agriculture during
the nineteenth century, both populations and standards of
living rose rapidly in the Western world. There was a
demand for larger populations to occupy and to exploit
the resources of the New World. Means of subsistence
increased faster than population growth. It is under-
standable that during this period of expansion and prosperity the gloomy predictions of Malthus were ignored:
it appeared that modern man might be able to escape the
Malthusian dilemma.

mal, produce progeny in great excess of the means of subsistence. Inevitably, most must die at an early age. It was largely these observations of Malthus that stimulated Darwin to formulate his theory of evolution. The excessive fecundity of nature led Darwin to conclude that there must be constant and continued competition and conflict in the " struggle for existence." The plants competed for soil, water, and light, while the animals competed for food. In the struggle for existence the weak and incompetent were suppressed or eliminated, while the more vigorous, aggressive, or adaptive plants and animals survived and multiplied. This " survival of the fittest " by " natural selection " led to change and evolution based only upon survival values.

Geological records show the evolutionary trends from simple to complex organisms. The successful species in the struggle for existence were sufficiently flexible to insure survival in a changing environment and in competition with other species. In most cases the original species and genera became extinct, but only after producing new forms which had a higher survival value. At all levels — whether from competition between individuals or between species, genera, or families — survival depended upon excessive progeny, success in competition for the means of subsistence, and the survival of the fittest.

" Positive " checks, associated with the ceaseless struggle for existence, are nature's method of controlling population growth. Fortunately man need not be ruled by nature's ruthless laws. He can choose the Malthusian " preventive " checks to control excessive population growth. Malthus said (69):

The preventive check, so far as it is voluntary, is peculiar to man, and arises from that distinctive superiority in his reasoning faculties which enables him to calculate distant consequences. The checks to the indefinite increase of plants and irrational animals are all either positive, or, if preventive, involuntary. But man cannot look around him, and see the distress which frequently presses upon those who have large families; he cannot contemplate his present possessions or earnings, which he now nearly consumes himself, and calculate the amount of each share, when with very little addition they must be divided, perhaps, among seven or eight, without feeling a doubt whether he follow the bent of his inclinations, he may be able to support the offspring which he will probably bring into the world.

Only man has been able to escape the inexorable law of nature. In most of the world, wild animals are no longer a menace to human life; clothing, housing, and fire permit adaptation to environments unfavorable to man's primitive ancestors; the domestication of plants and animals has increased his means of subsistence a hundredfold; the organization of government and law has given him greater security in his personal and economic life; industry has permitted much greater control of nature; modern medicine has extended the span of human life threefold; and man has learned how to control reproduction. Although war is still a serious menace and most of the world's people still live in poverty and ignorance, man has both the knowledge and the means of controlling his evolution without the overproduction of offspring destined to early death, without the incessant struggle for mere survival, and without natural selection based only upon brute strength, aggressiveness, and selfishness.

Although Malthus has often been accused of pessimism, he was optimistic about the immediate future of Europe.

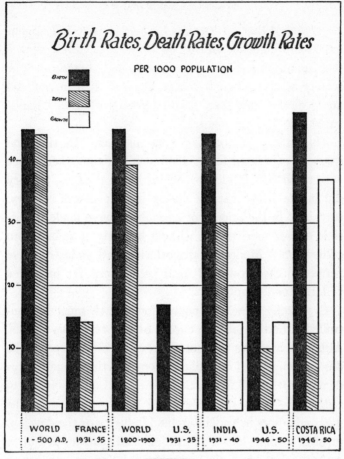

FIGURE 1

"POSITIVE CHECKS" OR "PREVENTIVE CHECKS"?

Population growth may be held down to a given rate either by the "positive check" of a high death rate (as in India) or by the "preventive check" of a low birth rate (as in the United States). If neither of these checks is in effect, the population growth will be virtually uncontrolled (as in Costa Rica).

Mankind must now choose which of the Malthusian checks is to control population growth — high death rates (from disease, famine, war, and natural catastrophe) or low birth rates.

(Data on early population growth from Julian Huxley; data for India from Kingsley Davis; recent vital statistics from the *Population Index*.)

He observed that " Europe is by no means so fully populated as it might be. In Europe there is the fairest chance
that human industry may receive its best direction. The
science of agriculture has been much studied in England
and Scotland; and there is still a great portion of unculti-
vated land in these countries."

This strain of optimism was justified. In rich and
sparsely populated areas, food supplies could keep pace
with rapid population growth for many decades, as they
did in the United States during the nineteenth century.
Advances in the science of agriculture have made it possible to feed more people without bringing more land into
cultivation. Modern transportation and industry have
permitted the growth of local populations far in excess
of local food supplies.

Eventually, however, population growth must be controlled either by positive checks or by preventive checks.
Although Malthus did not approve of contraception, he
did recommend " restraint " from marriage and " prudential restraint " in married life as preventive checks to
reduce the birth rate. He could not foresee all of the
great advances in agriculture and industry or the development of a more moral and rational attitude toward birth
control. Yet his basic laws of population growth are as
valid in our modern world as they were 150 years ago.

One might suppose that in a rational world religious
and political leaders would be unanimous in their approval of preventive rather than positive checks as a
means of controlling population growth. Strangely
enough, the growing interest in population problems has
been accompanied by renewed opposition to the Malthu-

sian doctrine — even more fanatic than in the past. The
two major opponents of effective preventive checks, as we
shall see in Chapter 10, are the Roman Catholic Church
and Communism.

The Catholic Church, which has long sponsored an
" expansionist " policy regarding human reproduction,
has opposed any rational and effective means of controlling the birth rate. A typical attitude toward the Malthusian doctrine is found in a pamphlet entitled *A Holy
War* published by the National Catholic Welfare Conference in 1942: " Perhaps the outstanding example today is the so-called neo-Malthusian or the well-known
practice of artificial birth control. . . . It is the practice
that is definitely related to the free love theory. It stems
from the latter, and from the largely discredited theory
of over population of Malthus." Even more emphatic is
the slogan " Birth control is against God's law," used as
the title of a pamphlet bearing the signature of Freder-
ick W. Mansfield, former mayor of Boston and legal coun-
sel for the late Cardinal O'Connell. William Thomas
Walsh in the August 1939 issue of the *Catholic World*
asserted that the United States could sustain " a future
population of unlimited size, practically speaking."

The opposition of the early Communists to the Malthusian doctrine was well summarized in 1922 by Margaret Sanger in her book *The Pivot of Civilization* (98):

A remarkable feature of early Marxian propaganda has been
the almost complete unanimity with which the implications of
the Malthusian doctrines have been derided, denounced, and
repudiated. Any defense of the so-called " Law of Population "
was enough to stamp one, in the eyes of the orthodox Marxians,
as a " tool of the capitalistic class," seeking to dampen the

ardor of those who expressed the belief that men might create a better world for themselves. Malthus, they claimed, was actuated by selfish class motives. He was not merely a hidebound aristocrat, but a pessimist who was trying to kill all hope of human progress. By Marx, Engels, Bebel, Kautsky and the celebrated leaders and interpreters of Marx's great " Bible of the Working Class " . . . birth control has been looked upon as a subtle Machiavellian sophistry created for the purpose of placing the blame for human misery elsewhere than at the door of the capitalistic class. Upon this point the orthodox Marxian mind has been universally and sternly uncompromising.

The modern Communists are still fanatically opposed to Malthusian concepts.

Although the Vatican and the Kremlin are the major opponents of the Malthusian doctrine, some opposition comes from other sources, including a few scientists, as we shall see in Chapter 9. Some people maintain that civilization tends to sterilize modern man and automatically provides the necessary preventive checks. Many scientists mention the Malthusian laws of population growth only in terms of positive checks; they refer to poor and densely populated countries as " Malthusian " areas — with the implication that more prosperous countries are not subject to the laws of population growth. Some scientists maintain that modern science can increase the world's resources to meet any possible demands. Kirtley Mather, in his book *Enough and to Spare* (70), concludes that " the gloomy prediction of Malthus does not now apply, and if present trends continue, never will apply to man." Alva Myrdal, senior director of the United Nations Department of Social Affairs and an able and distinguished Swedish sociologist, assures us that " the historical evidence thus goes entirely contrary to

Malthus' predictions, founded upon his theory " (73).

Nevertheless, a survey of the present world population provides convincing evidence of the validity of the Malthusian laws of population growth. Such an analysis shows that nearly two-thirds of the world's people still rely largely on positive checks to control excessive growth of populations. Less than 20 per cent of the world's people depend largely upon the preventive checks, and only these people have essentially completed the Demographic Transition — the transition from a culture with high birth rates, high death rates, and low living standards to a culture with low birth rates, low death rates, and relatively high living standards.

The present demographic status of the world is shown in Table 1. The first demographic group includes the people of North America, Western Europe, and Oceania (Australia and New Zealand). Although they contain only 15 per cent of the world population, these countries receive more than half of the world income, consume about two-thirds of the world's energy output from mineral fuels and hydroelectric power, and have a life expectancy of about sixty-five years. Although only about 20 per cent of their working population is engaged in agriculture, the food production is ample and the majority of the people are well fed. Both birth rates and death rates are relatively low. Population growth is greater than before World War II; but in most areas agricultural production has more than kept pace with population growth. Even though birth rates during recent years have been excessive in some areas, these countries have essentially completed their Demographic Transition.

The second demographic group includes the U.S.S.R.,

TABLE 1

DEMOGRAPHIC STATUS OF THE WORLD (1950)

	Demographic groups †			
	I	II	III	World
Population: millions (1950)	362	496	1550	2408
Population: percentage of world total	15	21	64	100
Annual income: billions of dollars	362	149	120	631
Annual income: percentage of world total	57	24	19	100
Annual income per person (1950 dollars)	1000	300	77	262
Energy consumption per person*	6	1	.25	....
Percentage of population in agriculture	20	50	70	57
Birth rates: per 1000 population	16–24	25–30	40–45	37
Death rates: per 1000 population	11	15	30	25
Annual population growth rate	1.1%	1.2%	1.2%	1.2%
Potential annual population growth rate (with modern death rates)	1.1%	1.5%	3.0%	2.5%

† Demographic GROUP I includes North America, Western Europe, Australia, and New Zealand. GROUP II includes the U.S.S.R., eastern and southern Europe, Japan, and Argentina. GROUP III includes Africa, Asia, the Middle East, and Latin America.

The classification of major demographic areas is largely that of Notestein and Thompson. It is also, with minor exceptions, the same as the classification used by the U.S. State Department in the "Point Four" program.

* Coal, oil, and hydroelectric energy in coal equivalent (tons per person).

Data from U.N. *Demographic Yearbook,* 1952; U.N. *Population Studies,* No. 17; U.N. *Statistical Papers,* Series H, No. 5 (1954); Woytinsky (128).

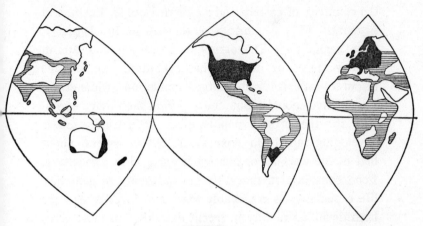

FIGURE 2

THE GEOGRAPHY OF HUNGER

According to Malthus, populations tend to increase faster than the means of subsistence; the increase must be controlled by positive checks or by preventive checks — by high death rates or by low birth rates. Most of the world's people have not yet adopted preventive checks; as a result, population growth outstrips the growth of food production.

Nearly two-thirds of the world's people do not get enough to eat (SHADED AREAS ABOVE). Their inadequate diets make them subject to nutritional deficiencies that sap their energy and lower their resistance to disease. Paradoxical as it may appear, the greatest hunger is in areas where most of the working population is engaged in agriculture.

Only in the industrialized countries are the people adequately nourished, although merely 20 to 30 per cent of the workers are farmers (BLACK AREAS ABOVE). Only in the industrial countries is population growth controlled by " preventive checks."

(Data from American Geographic Society, *A Study in Human Starvation.*)

the countries of eastern and southern Europe, Japan, and Argentina. These countries, as we shall see in Chapter 7, have begun their Demographic Transition and are in various stages of demographic evolution. Some have resources for considerably larger populations, while others do not have enough resources to permit high living standards for the present populations. Industrialization is developing rapidly in some areas, but in general about half of the working population is engaged in agriculture. Food consumption ranges from inadequate to generous, life expectancy is reasonably high, and birth rates have been declining rapidly in recent decades. In most areas (especially the U.S.S.R.) industrial production is increasing rapidly; but food production is hardly keeping pace with population growth. With the exception of Japan and several countries of southern Europe, all have adequate potential resources to support somewhat larger populations. Population growth in these countries is controlled by both positive and preventive checks. Any decline in birth rates is likely to be accompanied by declining death rates, and fairly rapid population growth can be expected for at least several decades. Birth rates in Japan and Italy, however, have been reduced rapidly in recent years.

The third demographic group includes most of the people of Asia, Africa, and Latin America, containing nearly two-thirds of the world population. In these countries industrialization has hardly begun — as shown by the per-capita consumption of energy. With an average per-capita income of only about $75 per year, these people live little above subsistence levels. Most of them are engaged in subsistence agriculture, and dietary standards are far below the levels necessary for good health. Life expectancy is less than half of that in the modern Western nations. Both birth rates and death rates are high; potential population growth is very high. In a few of these countries, public-health programs have reduced death rates to modern levels, with the result that populations are growing at the rate of about 3 per cent annually in spite of low living standards. In general the people of these demographic areas depend almost entirely on positive checks to control excessive population growth. For many decades any increase in industrial and agricultural production has been absorbed by population growth, and the end result is more people living in ignorance and poverty.

Modern man cannot escape the laws of population growth. Populations tend to increase faster than the means of subsistence and must be controlled either by the positive checks that increase death rates or by the preventive checks that reduce birth rates. A survey of world history provides ample proof that the Malthusian checks have always controlled the growth of human populations. Man can now choose which of the two checks he desires — high death rates or low birth rates.

2

The Growth of the Human Population

Man has lived on this earth for at least fifty thousand years, and his primitive ancestors for more than half a million years. Yet it was not until the sixteenth century of the Christian era that the human population reached half a billion. During the past three centuries, the world population has increased about fourfold. The increase over the past half-century has been nearly a billion (Table 2).

Obviously this recent population growth is unprece-

TABLE 2

WORLD POPULATION (1650–1950)

(in millions)

	1650 A.D.	1750	1800	1850	1900	1950 A.D.
Asia	330	479	602	749	937	1272
Europe			150	204	277	394
	100	140				
U.S.S.R.			37	62	113	200
Africa	100	95	90	95	120	199
North America	1	1	5	24	80	166
Latin America	12	11	20	35	75	162
Oceania	2	2	2	2	6	13
World	545	728	906	1171	1608	2406

Data from Cressey (24) and Dorn (30).

dented in human history. Even at the relatively modest growth rate of the nineteenth century — a rate of 0.6 per cent annually — world population would reach astronomical numbers in a few thousand years. For example, let us assume that the human race began with Adam and Eve in the year 4004 B.C. If their descendants had increased at the nineteenth-century rate, the population would have approached a billion by the year 1000 B.C.; at the beginning of the Christian era the population would have exceeded 1000 billion; in the year 1000 A.D. there would have been, literally, standing room only on the surface of the earth. Yet the growth rate during the nineteenth century was only about half what it is today — and only a fifth of the rate that has been attained by several countries during recent years.

During most of man's existence, high birth rates were nearly balanced by high death rates. Populations grew very slowly. Evidence from the distribution of blood groups among the modern races of man shows evidence of " genetic drift," indicating that at times the survival of the human species itself was reduced to the precarious survival of small and isolated groups. Even as late as the early Bronze and Iron Age, the expectancy of life was probably little more than eighteen years (71).

Early man, much like his anthropoid relatives, must have led a life largely devoted to hunting (or fighting) for his next meal and to avoiding his natural enemies. His food consisted of seeds, fruits, and tubers gathered from nature. Although he probably captured and ate some of the smaller animals, early man generally was the hunted and not the hunter. With uncertain and seasonal food supplies, with little or no protection from the weather, and with the most primitive means of fighting his natural enemies, man's death rates must have been very high.

The discovery of the use of fire and the invention of weapons were great advances in man's economic evolution. He could now cook hard seeds and tough meat, making them more digestible and palatable. Now that he had fire to warm his cave or hut, he could move into the colder areas of the temperate zone. Weapons enabled him to increase his food supply and to obtain skins for clothing and shelter. Fire and weapons provided some protection against the larger carnivorous animals. But man still lived a precarious life: food supplies were still uncertain; expanding populations led to tribal warfare; and man had as yet no control over disease.

Sir Arthur Keith has estimated that the maximum population which such a hunting and food-gathering economy could support could not exceed 20 million people. This estimate may be too liberal. The total Indian population of North America probably did not exceed a million, people largely dependent upon hunting, fishing, and food-gathering for their means of subsistence. With present agricultural techniques the United States and Canada could provide ample food for a population of 200 million, and a subsistence diet for nearly a billion. In many parts of the world agriculture is more productive in terms of yields per acre but living standards are, in general, considerably lower. Keeping in mind the variation in agricultural production and living standards throughout the world, we can conclude that agriculture now supports from 200 to 400 times as many people as the hunting and food-gathering culture did. Thus, before the art of agriculture was developed some six or eight thousand years ago (1), the world population may not have exceeded 6 to 12 million people.

The development of agriculture was the greatest contribution to man's economic and cultural development. Only with a productive agriculture was it possible to release a considerable part of the working population from the time-consuming task of providing subsistence for itself. Industry, transportation, education, and the arts and sciences all become possible with the release of adequate manpower from agricultural tasks. In most of the world, however, the great increase in food production provided by agriculture has been used to support larger populations at subsistence levels.

The earliest agriculture (as we shall see in Chapter 4) only supplemented the basic food supplies obtained by hunting, fishing, and food-gathering. As populations grew, they became more dependent upon cultivated crop plants and domesticated animals. Even with the continued expansion of agriculture and the development of urban communities, the populations grew slowly.*

Many factors kept the human populations from growing rapidly even after the advent of agriculture. Without the tools and techniques necessary to establish a perma-

---

* Julian Huxley (54) has estimated that by the year 3000 B.C. the world population probably numbered between 20 and 40 million. It increased to perhaps 100 million by 1000 B.C., and to 200 million early in the Christian era. Death rates must have been very high long after the development of agriculture. It was not until the sixteenth century that world population passed 500 million, and not until late in the eighteenth century did it exceed 800 million.

nent agriculture on grasslands and forested areas, the cultivation of crops was largely limited to the flood plains of the great rivers. In the uplands, agriculture was based upon the domestication of animals. The limited cultivated areas and the low productivity of primitive livestock farming could not produce enough food for the expanding populations. It was inevitable that conflict should develop between the roving and aggressive nomads and the more prosperous and sedentary inhabitants of the towns and neighboring farms. Nomadic raids continued for thousands of years, up to the thirteenth century when the hordes of Genghis Khan overran both Asia and Europe.

As populations grew, agriculture had to produce more food either by bringing new land into cultivation or by increasing the yields of the land already in cultivation. New land usually meant poorer land. The cultivation of mountain slopes after the clearing of natural vegetation led to erosion and loss of soil. With the loss of forests, the spring floods became more violent and often destroyed crops in the fertile valleys. In much of the world today, denuded hills and mountains bear mute testimony to the results of population pressure.

With further population growth, little new land was available for agricultural expansion. The farms were divided into smaller units and worked more intensively. Soon it was no longer possible to grow soiling crops to replenish the fertility of the soil. Organic matter, including human excrement, had to be brought to the fields to maintain crop production. Eventually the utmost labor provided a meager subsistence diet inadequate to sustain good health. Many died of diseases promoted by malnutrition. When there was inadequate rainfall or when the spring floods failed to restore soil fertility, many died of starvation.

The concentration of people in villages and cities was made possible by a more productive agriculture; but the concentration in turn fostered high death rates. Towns and cities of the Middle Ages were filthy by modern standards; the lack of sanitation in the preparation of food and in the disposal of sewage undoubtedly made the town resident more subject to disease and pestilence than his rural cousins or the inhabitants of small villages. Pestilence was prevalent in ancient urban communities. Later, the notorious " Black Death " of the fourteenth century spread through Asia and Europe with devastating effects; it has been estimated that between a quarter and a half of the population of England was wiped out by this epidemic. In England during the Middle Ages the expectancy of life had reached only thirty-five years (71). And even this was twice that of Greece during the early Bronze and Iron Age several thousand years earlier. In most of the world, however, death rates were little lower during most of the agricultural era than they had been during the tens of thousands of years when man depended upon food-gathering and hunting for his means of subsistence.

It is little wonder that our ancestors in Europe during the Middle Ages chanted the Litany: " From lightning and tempest, from plague, pestilence and famine, from battle and murder, and from sudden death, Good Lord deliver us." With the aid of science, a steadily increased deliverance from plague, pestilence, and famine has come about. By 1850 the expectancy of life in England had increased to about forty-one years. With more rapid progress in agriculture and industry during the second half of the nineteenth century, aided by some progress in medicine and sanitation, the expectancy of life in several countries had increased by 1900 to fifty years. Recent rapid advances in industry and medical science have increased life expectancies to more than sixty-five years in the countries of Western Europe, North America, and Oceania. Other parts of the world have benefited from the development of agricultural and industrial techniques, and especially from the control of epidemics in recent decades.

But this " deliverance " has also encouraged unprecedented population growth. Between 1800 and 1900, the world population increased from little more than 900 million to slightly over 1600 million. The spectacular growth rates of the past few hundred years raised the total number to 2400 million by 1950 and to nearly 2500 million only four years later.*

* During the food-gathering era (which may have lasted for at least 30 thousand years), the world population increased at an average rate of between 0.03 and 0.04 per cent annually, with, of course, considerable fluctuation. The average annual growth rate of the hunting and early agricultural cultures was little higher — about 0.04 per cent (54). Even with the development of agriculture and the founding of towns, the annual growth rate increased to a mere 0.05 per cent. From the beginning of the Christian era to 1500 A.D., it reached little more than 0.07 per cent. During the next 300 years there was a more rapid increase, averaging perhaps as much as 0.2 per cent. During the nineteenth century it averaged 0.6 per cent, and from 1900 to 1950 the average reached 0.75 per cent. It was about 1.0 per cent by 1950 and by 1953 probably exceeded 1.2 per cent. The effect of these growth rates on population increase from 5000 B.C. to 1950 A.D. is shown in Figure 3.

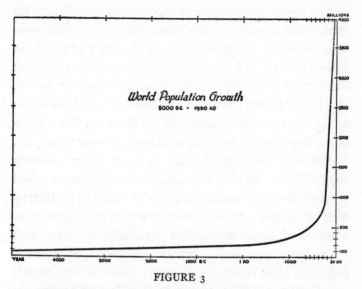

FIGURE 3

WORLD POPULATION GROWTH (5000 B.C. to 1950 A.D.)

The human population grew very slowly as long as man depended upon hunting and food-gathering for subsistence. With uncertain food supplies, little protection against natural enemies, and no control of disease, death rates were high and the expectancy of life was less than twenty years. Even with the advent of agriculture (eight or ten thousand years ago) life was still precarious and death rates remained high. During man's early history, population growth could not have exceeded .03 per cent or .04 per cent per year.

Although advances in agriculture and transportation permitted more rapid population growth, the growth rate of the world population probably did not reach 0.1 per cent annually until after the beginning of the Christian era. Some increase occurred before the Industrial Revolution, and the growth rate was about 0.3 per cent in the eighteenth century. Since 1800 the rate of population growth has increased rapidly until it now exceeds 1.0 per cent annually. In some countries, the combination of natural birth rates with modern death rates has resulted in population increases of nearly 3.0 per cent annually. At the present rate of increase, the world population may exceed 4,000 million by the end of this century.

(Data for early growth rates from Julian Huxley; for recent rates from Dorn.)

The recent growth rate of the world population is far from the maximum that has been attained in certain countries for short periods of time. In the early years of the United States, death rates were relatively low because there were ample resources, the population was young, and there was no great concentration of people in urban areas. For several decades, as we have seen, the population increased at the rate of about 3 per cent per year.

Although the vital statistics in most Latin-American countries are not very reliable, the fertility ratios based upon recent census returns indicate similar extraordinarily high birth rates. Most of these countries have birth rates in excess of 40 per thousand of population and may reach 50 or more in a few countries. Modern public-health programs often reduce death rates rapidly without having any immediate effect on the birth rates. The average annual growth rate for Central America was slightly over 2 per cent for the years 1946–50, and 3 per cent in several countries in recent years.*

A population growth of 3 per cent annually would double the population in twenty-four years; one of 2 per cent in thirty-five years; one of 1 per cent in seventy years; even one of 0.5 per cent would double a population in 140 years.

It is evident that no country could long maintain a

---

* El Salvador, one of the most overpopulated and poorest countries in Central America, had a reported birth rate of 48.5 and a death rate of 14.7 — a net population increase of 3.38 per cent in 1950. In more prosperous Costa Rica, the reported birth rate was 54.6 in 1952. From the reported death rate of 11.6, the population would seem to have increased 4.3 per cent in a single year. In Mexico, where the vital statistics are more reliable, birth rates of 45.7 and death rates of 16.2 in 1950 produced an annual growth of nearly 3 per cent (83).

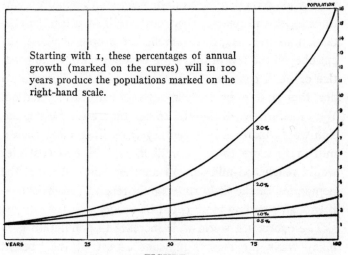

Starting with 1, these percentages of annual growth (marked on the curves) will in 100 years produce the populations marked on the right-hand scale.

FIGURE 4

POTENTIAL POPULATION GROWTH

Today few countries have growth rates as low as 0.5 per cent annually; yet it was not until the nineteenth century that world population growth rates reached this modest level. At this rate of growth it would take about 140 years for a population to double in number. At the 1950 rate of world population growth (about 1 per cent annually) the population would increase threefold in a century.

In a number of countries, growth rates are nearly 3 per cent annually. Such growth rates, if they could be continued for a hundred years, would result in a sixteenfold increase in population. If such a rate continues in Central America, the population will increase from 50 million in 1950 to 800 million a century later.

China claims a population of 600 million and a growth rate of more than 2 per cent annually. At this rate China's population would in a century reach nearly 5 billion — twice the present population of the whole world.

Without a controlled birth rate, poverty, starvation, and high death rates are inevitable. Excessive population growth is the greatest obstacle to peace and prosperity in the world today.

population growth of more than 1 per cent annually; continued growth rates of 3 per cent would soon lead to fantastic numbers. If, for example, the people of Connecticut obeyed the law in that state which prohibits the practice of birth control, the birth rate might well reach 40 per thousand even in a relatively mature population. With modern death rates of 10 per thousand, the population would increase in a century from little more than 2 million to more than 32 million, and in two centuries would reach 500 million. In another hundred years the population of the little state would reach 8000 million — if enough standing room could be found.

The enormous, world-wide increase in population is in many ways the most significant aspect of the present world scene. It is central to the concern of this study. Even a brief look at the main areas that will presumably undergo the Demographic Transition in the future (although it is difficult to foresee just how they are to do so) will reveal the colossal difficulties to be overcome, chiefly the ever-increasing populations in areas already burdened by very low standards of living. In most of Asia, for example, birth rates are near the physiological maximum, while death rates are higher than those of England in the Middle Ages. Three-fourths of the Asian peoples are still engaged in subsistence agriculture. These people are good farmers, but they lack the needed land, fuel, equipment, fertilizer, fungicides, and insecticides to produce food in quantities large enough to release manpower for industrial and educational development. Any increase in the means of subsistence must be used to support more people at subsistence levels without any significant increase in living standards. Today more than half of the world's people live in Asia. But they live neither well nor long. Death rates take a heavy toll.

Gerald F. Winfield, a medical missionary who spent many years in China, has presented a pathetic picture of life and death in that country: " Almost every day in most of the modern hospitals of China pregnant mothers give a history of from five to twelve, or even fifteen, pregnancies from which they have one or two children still alive, and frequently none at all " (127). According to Winfield, 75 per cent of all deaths in China are due to preventable diseases which in Western nations are under control. Contamination from human excrement, resulting from primitive ignorant habits and from the use of human manure as a fertilizer for farm crops, causes some 4 million deaths each year.

In both China and India the balance between food supplies and population pressure is so precarious that any decrease in food production results in famine. Droughts, floods, and insect plagues frequently destroy crops over large areas. As a result, millions die of starvation or from disease imposed by malnutrition. In the Indian famine of 1877, 4 million people starved to death; the influenza epidemic of 1918 killed between 15 and 20 million Indians. Even in normal times, half of the children born do not live long enough to contribute to the production of means of subsistence. Those who survive are subject to malaria, intestinal parasites, tuberculosis, and other diseases which sap their energy. Their diet consists of less than a pound of grain per day, supplemented by a few vegetables. Yet in spite of these " positive checks " the population continues to grow. The average growth rate for Asia during the year 1950 was 1.2 per cent.

Africa's demographic status is a peculiar one. With a few exceptions it is not overpopulated — and yet living standards there are little better than they are in Asia. Disease and malnutrition are prevalent in most of the " dark continent." The somewhat better diets have only recently led to accelerated population growth. The population remained at about 100 million from 1650 to 1850 (partly because of the slave trade). During the past century it has doubled, and during recent years it has been growing at the rate of about 1 per cent per year. Africa has adequate resources for a more productive agriculture and industry, but mental and physical inertia, perhaps initiated or aggravated by the colonial status of much of the area, seems to be the major factor in the lack of development.

Latin America is a region of great demographic variation. Some areas have attained relatively high living standards and low death rates, while others have hardly emerged from a hunting and food-gathering culture. In general, however, living standards are low and birth rates are high. Most of the people are engaged in subsistence agriculture. Public-health programs have reduced death rates to low levels, even in countries where malnutrition is prevalent. Some countries have resources sufficient to provide adequate living standards, but others will do well if they can provide a good life for present numbers. Growth rates in Latin America, as we have seen, are very high; for the years 1946–50, the population of South

America grew at the rate of 1.8 per cent per year and that of Central America at the rate of 2.1 per cent (114).

The relatively high living standards of our Western nations have shown the rest of the world that poverty is not inevitable. The poor peoples of the world are becoming restless. The inevitable and increasing impact of our civilization upon the rest of the world not only spreads material and cultural advantages but also by decreasing death rates, helps to increase the problems of population pressure. Population pressure and low living standards are probably the most explosive forces in the world today. Must these hungry and illiterate people await the same slow evolutionary economic and social stages as the European peoples have gone through? In the face of inadequate lands and other resources, it would seem that a miracle would be needed to bring about such a change.

Much of the progress of the Western nations has been based upon expanding frontiers of natural resources in the New World, accompanied by great progress in industrial and agricultural techniques. Can the new frontiers of industrial and social progress compensate for the lack of adequate land and mineral resources in the densely populated areas of the world? These are some of the problems to be considered in subsequent chapters.

3

The Demographic Transition

Less than 20 per cent of the world's people have completed the Demographic Transition and achieved generally high living standards. A high standard of living, needless to say, means more than an adequate diet: industry, art, education, and science, as well as agriculture, are among the standards of measurement. Only the people of the modern Western nations have adopted the Malthusian " preventive checks " which allow low death rates and high living standards. Checks specifically aimed at controlling population growth are essential at some point if a nation is to effect the Demographic Transition; in the Western nations such checks followed, rather than preceded, higher living standards and lower death rates.

Most of the world has still to make the Demographic Transition; without it there can be no hope for the Four Freedoms for all mankind. Can the rest of the world make the transition by repeating the pattern established by the Western nations? To envision the demographic prospects of the world as a whole, it is essential to examine carefully the Demographic Transition of Western Europe. Several of the paths of escape from excessive population pressure taken by the Western nations are, as we shall see, no longer open to the peoples of Asia, Africa,

and South America. Succeeding chapters will further
examine the possibilities open to these latter areas.

The people of Western Europe were able to make the
Demographic Transition because of the development of
agriculture and industry, aided by the expanding frontiers
of the New World. In order of sequence, the paths of
escape from excessive population pressure and the Malthusian " positive checks " were as follows:

(1) *Advances in agriculture,* which increased food pro-
    duction and released manpower for industry.

(2) *Industrialization,* which provided equipment for
    agriculture, transportation, and communication.

(3) *Emigration,* which relieved population pressure in
    the home country and permitted exploitation of
    new resources.

(4) *Colonial empires,* which provided raw materials
    for industrial countries and markets for manu-
    factured products.

(5) *Modern medicine,* which reduced death rates and
    improved the general health of the people.

(6) *Control of birth rates,* which prevented excessive
    population growth.

An analysis of the general significance and interrela-
tion of these " paths of escape " will lay the foundation
for a more specific examination of the Demographic
Transition in certain European countries.

(1) An efficient agriculture is the foundation of our
modern civilization. Before 1700 agriculture was the
major occupation in all parts of the world. A primitive
and inefficient agriculture required the labor of three-
fourths of the working population to produce the needed

food. In 1700 there had been little advance in agricultural techniques for several thousand years. Farm practices were so similar in all parts of the civilized world that the European farmer transplanted to Asia would have been familiar with the general methods of cultivation and the treatment of the soil. Considerable progress in agriculture was made during the eighteenth century with the introduction of iron plows and cultivating machinery, but the foundations of modern agriculture were not developed until the second half of the nineteenth century.

At the beginning of the Demographic Transition (about 1800), Europe was not densely populated. With adequate land, a generally fertile soil, and an equable climate, European farmers could develop a very productive agriculture without undue exploitation of soil resources or of manpower. A more efficient agriculture produced the needed food for a rapidly growing population; more important still, it released men for work in industry, art, and science. When most people are engaged in producing food for their own consumption, living standards must remain low; needed labor for the development of industry, transportation, education, communication, and public health becomes available only with the release of men from agriculture.

At the beginning of the Demographic Transition more than three-fourths of the people of Western Europe were engaged in food production; now less than a third are farmers. In England, farmers constitute less than 10 per cent of all workers, but England is only 50 per cent self-sufficient in food production in spite of her efficient and productive agricultural program. In the United States less than 20 per cent of the working population are farmers; 10 per cent could raise all the food we need with proper equipment and other aids, with some to spare.

(2) Industrialization has developed efficient methods of producing clothing, tools, transportation, and housing. It has provided the machinery for a more efficient agriculture, the chemical fertilizers for increased crop production, and the transportation facilities for the distribution of agricultural products. The development of power machinery has greatly increased man's efficiency in both agriculture and industry. The release of human labor by machinery has permitted even greater developments in education, the arts and sciences, and higher living standards for all.

The development of industry has had two major effects on population growth in Europe. It has promoted the growth of large cities, where incentives for large families are reduced. It has also permitted general population growth far in excess of the domestic resources of individual countries. Although Europe has developed a very efficient agriculture, with yields per acre more than twice that of the world as a whole, food production has not been able to keep pace with the rapid population growth. For many decades most European nations have had to import food from other countries; even before World War I, Germany and France imported about a fourth of their food, England and Italy about 40 per cent, and Belgium nearly 60 per cent (32).

Industrial development has allowed these countries to import food in exchange for industrial products. It has

also provided the efficient transportation necessary to import food and raw products into the industrial countries,
and to export manufactured products to industrially undeveloped areas.

(3) Not only did the frontiers of the Western world
provide food for Europe's growing population, raw material for her industries, and markets for her manufactured products, but also they relieved population pressure
by absorbing millions of emigrants. Since the beginning
of the nineteenth century, more than 60 million Europeans have migrated to the Americas, Australia, and
South Africa. During the past three hundred years, the
local population of Europe (not including the U.S.S.R.)
has increased by about 300 million people; yet there live
in countries outside of Europe nearly 400 million more
of European descent. If Europe had had to support all
its descendants, living standards there now would be at
little more than subsistence levels. Without emigration
and the resources of the New World, it is improbable
that Europe would have completed its Demographic
Transition. In an analysis of the role of the New World
in Europe's development, Walter Prescott Webb concludes that "without this frontier modern Europe would
have been so different from what it is today that it could
hardly be considered modern at all" (124).

But emigration helped to reduce population pressure
in most of the countries of Europe only where it was accompanied by a decreasing birth rate. Where birth rates
remained relatively high, emigration, even on a large
scale, was not effective in reducing population pressure.
In 1800 Italy had a population of little more than 17 mil-

lion; since 1800 at least 17 million Italians have migrated to other lands. Yet the population of Italy has grown rapidly. In 1950 Italy's population had reached 46 million, and it was increasing by about 400,000 per year. Today Italy is grossly overpopulated in relation to its agricultural and industrial resources; with the exception of Austria, Spain, and the Balkan areas, the Italians have the lowest standard of living in Europe.

In Ireland, on the other hand, emigration was very effective in relieving population pressure and permitted a great increase in the standard of living. Between 1650 and 1841 the population increased from about 1 million to more than 8 million, an average increase of about 1.2 per cent annually. R. N. Salaman believes that the use of the potato as the major food crop was responsible for much of the misery and catastrophe in Ireland during the eighteenth and nineteenth centuries. The potato was so well adapted to Ireland's soil and climate that it provided the maximum amount of food with a minimum expenditure of labor. Says Dr. Salaman (96):

> The more the potato fulfilled the requirements of the household, the sooner was endeavor damped down, and sloth and slovenliness exalted. As time went on, the sequence — poverty, potatoes, larger families, more potatoes, and greater poverty, became ever more firmly established, till nothing but revolution or catastrophe could break it.

Catastrophe came when the potato blight destroyed the crops in 1845 and subsequent years. A million people died of starvation and more than a million people migrated from Ireland between 1846 and 1851. About 5 million have migrated to the United States since 1820,

and it has been estimated that there are about twelve
million people of predominantly Irish descent in this
country today.   The potato famine not only initiated
large-scale emigration but probably played an important
part in the decline in the birth rate.   Birth rates started
to decline as early as 1800, but the painful experiences
of crop failure and famine clearly demonstrated the consequences of attempting to raise large families on little
land.   Marriage rates declined and the marriage age increased, with a resulting decline in birth rates.   As a result of the potato famine, wholesale emigration, and the
decline of the birth rate, the population of Ireland, including Ulster, declined from more than 8 million in 1844
to 4.4 million in 1950.   During the past 150 years, then,
emigration has played an important part in the demographic evolution of Ireland, but largely in conjunction
with the rapidly declining birth rate.   The Irish today
enjoy a standard of living nearly twice as high as that of
Italy — because of Italy's failure to reduce her birth rates
during the period of major emigration.

(4) Colonial empires provided the industrial countries
both with raw materials and with markets for their manufactured products.   For instance, the English sent textiles
to India in exchange for foods and fibers, and various industrial products to Egypt, Australia, and Canada in exchange for cotton, wool, and wheat.   In many cases, of
course, colonial exploitation brought food and raw materials into Europe with little exchange.   World-wide industrial monopolies, coupled with a certain parasitic
economic dependence upon the backward areas of the
world, allowed many European nations to support, at

relatively high living standards, populations far in excess
of local domestic resources.

(5) The control of death rates has been the major
cause of Europe's rapid population growth during the past
few centuries. Death rates declined more rapidly than
birth rates, so that even large-scale emigration could not
effectively reduce the rapid population growth. During
the past century, Europe's population has nearly doubled.
Before the seventeenth century, high birth rates were balanced by high death rates, and populations grew slowly.
With the increase in food supplies and the development
of modern medicine, the death rates declined from about
30 per thousand in the seventeenth century to less than
12 per thousand in 1950.

Even before the introduction of modern medicine and
public health, death rates were being gradually reduced
by improved living conditions and better diets. Although
Jenner found in 1798 that smallpox could be controlled
by vaccination, it was nearly a century later that Pasteur
and Koch established the relationship between bacteria
and disease and not until recent decades that most com-
municable diseases were brought under control. New
techniques followed quickly; the recent discoveries of
penicillin, aureomycin, and other antibiotics only touch
on the possibilities for control of disease. In many countries today the expectancy of life is approaching " three
score years and ten," compared with about thirty-five
years during the Middle Ages in Europe and less than
twenty years during the Bronze and Iron Ages in Greece.

(6) The Demographic Transition of Europe would have
been impossible without control of the birth rate. The

decline of the birth rate can be studied under two aspects, the motives and the means. The motives are of primary importance and are diverse in their nature. In general, urbanization of the population has been a major factor in motivation. The farmer could utilize child labor in many ways, and the problem of adequate food and clothing for a large family was less acute on the farm. There was usually ample space in the farmhouse and many things of interest in the countryside to keep the children occupied before they were called on to work in the barns and fields. In the city, space was limited both at home and in the streets. With the abolition of 'child labor in factories, the children became an economic liability; with compulsory education, their period of economic dependency was increased.

Urban life also led to greater competition. The demand for better houses, better clothes, and more freedom conflicted with the desire for more children. The demand for better education of the children led to smaller families. Potential children had to compete with the complex apparatus of modern life: cars, refrigerators, television sets. The emancipation of women and their participation in business and industry has also reduced birth rates. Long-term professional training for both men and women often either delays the age of marriage or causes the wife to work until the husband completes his training and is established in a business or profession.

The cost of rearing and educating a child makes it difficult for the average couple to support more than a few children. According to L. I. Dublin of the Metropolitan Life Insurance Company (31), before World War II

the cost of raising a child to the age of eighteen, in the
$2 500-per-year income bracket, was about $400 annually.
Obviously most married couples cannot provide the
needed housing, food, clothing, education, and medical
care for more than a few children.

Nor is it now necessary for mothers to bear seven or
eight children to insure the survival of two or three.

The availability of artificial means for controlling the
birth rate have been of less importance than the motives.
If the motives are sufficiently strong, the simplest methods are adequate to reduce the birth rate. In Ireland and
to a lesser extent in Sweden, where birth rates are among
the lowest in Europe, major factors are the fewness of
marriages and the lateness of marriages. In Sweden and
rural France the contraceptive technique most commonly
used is one of the most primitive. Although contraceptive
techniques were known in earliest historical times, the
modern mechanical and chemical contraceptives have
been available for less than a hundred years. These
modern contraceptives are more effective than primitive
methods — but only with adequate motivation. These
contraceptives are not effective at low levels of motivation and cannot control irresponsible reproduction.

In the countries of Europe, birth rates before 1800 were
more than 30 per thousand of population and death rates
were more than 25 per thousand. By 1850 there had been
some decline in birth rates, but a greater decline in the
death rates. Both birth and death rates declined more
rapidly during the next fifty years. Before World War II,
birth rates had declined to less than 16 per thousand in
England, France, Germany, and the Scandinavian coun-

tries. But death rates were even lower (about 12 per thousand), and populations continued to grow even in countries with birth rates below permanent replacement levels, because of the age structure of the populations.

The spurt in the birth rate in all of the Western nations after World War II increased birth rates in Western Europe to over 20 per thousand in many countries, but the rates have declined again.* Nearly all of the countries of Western Europe have or are approaching birth rates which, as the populations mature, will soon be in equilibrium with the low death rates. Although many of these countries are overpopulated in relation to domestic resources, there would be no excessive population pressure if they could look forward to a peaceful world and a united Europe, in which they could expand the new frontiers of science.

The various factors that contributed to the Demographic Transition of Western Europe were interrelated, but their relative importance varied considerably in different countries. The release of population pressure by emigration was an important factor in England and Ireland, but not in France. Colonial empires were an important asset for England, but of little value to Germany. An improved agriculture was of basic importance in all countries, particularly during the development of industrialization. Industrialization also was of major importance, and its effect on the transition was reflected in many ways. It raised the living standards, reduced the rural population, and indirectly reduced the birth rates. It also permitted

* The average in 1950 was down to 18 per thousand, with birth rates of less than 17 per thousand in Belgium, Sweden, England, and Germany (83). Even Italy's birth rate had dropped to 17.6 in 1952.

population growth in some countries far in excess of domestic natural resources. The reduction in the birth rate was of primary importance, even though it tended to follow rather than to precede the decline in the death rate and the general rise in living standards.

The fact that about 20 per cent of the world's population have been able to make the Demographic Transition has led many people to assume that the same general pattern will be followed by the rest of the world. Before considering the possibilities of a similar demographic evolution in other lands (see Chapter 7), we shall examine more carefully the transition in three European countries — England, Sweden, and France. We shall find that some of their "paths of escape" are now partially or completely blocked, and that the present available paths open to the people of Asia, Africa, and Latin America are long and steep.

When England began her transition at the end of the eighteenth century, she had relatively high birth rates and death rates. The high birth rates continued until 1850 and then declined at an increasing rate until the years preceding World War II. The recent post-war rise was temporary, and birth rates declined to 15.7 in 1952. The death rates had already started to decline before 1800; in general they continued to decline until 1950, when they were about 12 per thousand. During this period of 150 years, the excess of births over deaths led to rapid population growth — from about 10 million in 1800 to more than 50 million in 1950. This increase in population and the higher living standards during the period of transition were made possible by improved agriculture, industrial development, food imports, a colonial empire, and control of the birth rate.

Without the frontiers of the New World to provide food and raw materials and the space for emigrants, it is doubtful if the transition would have been possible. Emigration from England began soon after the discovery of America, and Robert Cook (22) estimates that more than 100 million people of English descent now live in other lands, primarily the United States, Canada, and Australia. The early English emigrants to the United States had higher birth rates and lower death rates than their relatives in England; but even at the more moderate growth rate in England the absence of emigration would have put a severe strain on the productive capacity of the country. England now finds it difficult to support a population of 50 million, but it would be impossible to support 150 million even at subsistence living standards. Since 1800 England's population has increased fivefold and all the people of English descent tenfold.

Sweden was able to make the Demographic Transition without a colonial empire and with only moderate emigration. Birth rates declined earlier than in England but death rates remained about the same, so that the population of Sweden grew more slowly. It increased only about threefold between 1800 and 1950, and emigration was not a major factor in this relatively slow growth. About a million Swedes migrated to America (but later than the major English migration); there are probably no more than 3 or 4 million people of Swedish descent in the United States and Canada. It is probable that the population of Swedish people in the world has not increased

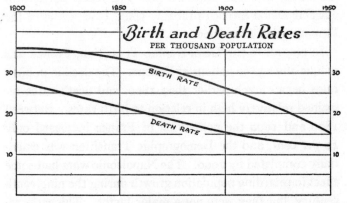

FIGURE 5

THE DEMOGRAPHIC TRANSITION IN ENGLAND

The transition from a high-birth-rate, high-death-rate culture (with low living standards) to a low-birth-rate, low-death-rate culture (with high living standards) took about 150 years in the countries of Western Europe. Even before 1800, both birth rates and death rates had declined considerably; but the Demographic Transition really began with the advent of industrialization. The increased agricultural efficiency released manpower for industry, and in turn the products of industry aided agriculture. With more food, better housing, and control of disease and epidemics, the death rates gradually declined. Birth rates declined more slowly and the result was a period of relatively rapid population growth. In recent decades both birth rates and death rates have reached low levels and the population is again growing slowly; but the people enjoy relatively high living standards and a longer expectancy of life.

more than fivefold during the past 150 years. Even without emigration Sweden probably could have achieved the
Demographic Transition.

√ In respect to the Demographic Transition, France was
unique among the nations of Europe. The decline in birth
rates began much earlier than 1800, and death rates remained relatively high in relation to birth rates. Between
1800 and 1900 the population of France increased only
40 per cent, and the Demographic Transition was essentially completed by 1900. The Napoleonic wars had some
effect in retarding population growth during the nineteenth
century, but they were not a major factor. The early reduction of the birth rate at a time when death rates were
not readily controlled accounts for the slow growth of the
French population during the transition. It is probable
that during the transition the population of France did
not increase more than twofold.

The early and rapid decline in the birth rate in France
must be attributed to the early development of motives
for a small family. There is no evidence that the decline
in the birth rate was due to lowered inherent fecundity.
As shown in Chapter 1 above, the French who went to
Canada set the world's record in fecundity over a period
of several hundred years.

In Western Europe, then, the Demographic Transition
began with a decline in the death rate; the decline of the
birth rate lagged about 75 to 100 years. In England, for
example, the death rate had declined to about 21 in 1850,
but the birth rate did not decline to that level until about
1925. For Western Europe in general, the transition from
high birth and death rates to low birth and death rates
took about 150 years. The decrease in the death rate

was not rapid compared with modern times, and growth rates increased, gradually reaching a peak at about 1.5 per cent annually. After several decades the growth rates began to decline, as birth rates decreased. Eventually, low death rates were balanced by low birth rates. Most of the countries of Western Europe are approaching a demographic equilibrium and the end of rapid population growth — although only France has reached an essentially stationary population.

During the Demographic Transition, over a period of about 150 years, populations (disregarding emigrants) have increased from a " low " of about twofold in France to a " high " of about fivefold in England. For most of Europe the total increase was about threefold, with a similar increase of Europeans in other lands. It is this inevitable increase in population growth during the Demographic Transition which makes difficult a similar transition in Africa and South America. It is difficult to imagine the successful achievement of the Demographic Transition in Asia if the local population must increase threefold.

Even though Europe was not densely populated at the beginning of the Demographic Transition, it had neither land nor domestic resources sufficient to provide for all of the great increase in population growth during the transition. With the opening of three continents for European settlement, and the exploitation of two others, Europe was able to provide for a rapidly growing population both at home and abroad. Walter Prescott Webb (124) has pointed out that the former frontiers are now as densely populated as Europe was in 1650. The land frontiers were increased about sixfold and populations of

European origin have increased nearly eightfold during
the past three hundred years.   There are no new frontiers
of any appreciable size.

The New World opened up great opportunities for population growth.   The immigrants to the Americas found
abundant farm land, vast tracts of virgin forests, and
great deposits of coal and iron ore; fertile land and timber were available to all.   A rural population was safer
from plagues and epidemics than the more urban population of Europe, and there was ample food.   Relative security and a rural society led to early marriage and
high birth rates; most of the immigrants were young and
brought with them the tradition of large families.   Unlike
the countries of Europe, the United States did not begin
its Demographic Transition with high birth rates nearly
balanced by high death rates.   Throughout most of the
period of demographic development, birth rates declined
more rapidly than death rates, but relatively low death
rates permitted a continued rapid growth of population.
This natural growth plus heavy immigration from Europe
increased the population from about 5 million in 1800 to
more than 150 million in 1950 — a thirtyfold increase in
150 years.   Canada and Australia have experienced similar development and population growth, though on a
smaller scale.

The countries of Western Europe, North America, and
Oceania have essentially completed their Demographic
Transition.   Several of the European countries have populations in excess of domestic resources, but in most of
the Western nations agriculture and industrial production
are more than keeping pace with population growth.

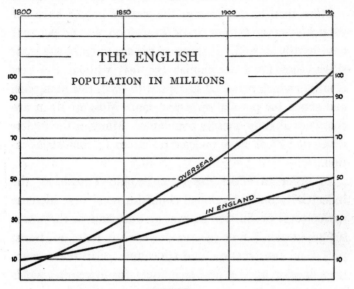

FIGURE 6

EMIGRATION AND THE DEMOGRAPHIC TRANSITION

During the Demographic Transition of the Western nations, the decline in the death rate without a corresponding decline in the birth rate has led to rapid population growth. With few exceptions no country has completed the transition with less than a threefold increase in population.

In 1800 England had a population of about 10 million; population pressure had been reduced by emigration, and about 5 million people of English origin were living overseas. England began her transition with ample land; for many decades she enjoyed an industrial monopoly which permitted imports of food and raw materials, and her colonies absorbed some of the population. In 150 years the population increased to about 50 million, and the overseas population to about 100 million by 1950 — a fivefold increase in England, plus a tenfold increase in people of English descent.

It is this rapid population growth during the Demographic Transition that makes it difficult, if not impossible, for many nations to follow the same paths of escape from poverty.

Only these countries have relatively high living standards.

More than 80 per cent of the world's people have not yet achieved the Demographic Transition, and 60 per cent have hardly started. If these people are to make the transition, they must accomplish the feat without the new frontiers which provided Europe with food, raw materials, and space for population expansion. Most of them are countries already densely populated. Many of the underdeveloped areas have meager resources for industrialization.

In order to effect the Demographic Transition, the industrially underdeveloped countries must first increase agricultural production so that at least half of the working population can be released for work in industry, transportation, construction, and education. Can these countries develop agricultural techniques for increasing yields per acre, and do they have enough arable land for an adequate agriculture? If not, can the new frontiers of science find other sources of food? At least a moderate degree of industrialization is essential to supply machines and equipment for agriculture, transportation, and construction. Have these countries the necessary sources of energy and the raw materials needed for an industrial culture?

We shall begin in the next chapters to consider the prospects for the Demographic Transition in the underdeveloped countries of the world by making a survey of the world's agricultural resources, followed by a survey of the world's industrial resources and the prospects for new sources of food and energy.

PART TWO

THE MATERIAL RESOURCES

4
Food for the World

Never in human history have all of the world's people had enough to eat. Primitive man spent most of his time hunting or fighting for his next meal. The development of agriculture in some parts of the world has made it possible, in these areas, to increase food production several hundred times above that of a hunting and food-gathering culture. Yet today nearly two-thirds of the world's people still subsist on inadequate diets. In most of the world, any increase in food production has been used to support growing populations. Problems of maintaining subsistence have precluded any improvement in dietary standards.

More than half of the present population of the world subsists on less than 2200 calories per day per person. The Food and Agriculture Organization of the United Nations recommends a minimum intake of 2650 calories; 3200 calories is the average for people of the United States. However, the variation in dietary standards is only partly expressed by these comparisons of calorie consumption. The low-calorie diets of the world in general are derived almost entirely from plant sources — cereals, tubers, and legumes. The high-calorie diets of the United States include liberal amounts of meat, milk, and eggs.

The production of food in these forms requires an

average of six or seven times as much arable land as the production of comparable amounts of calories and proteins in the form of cereals, tubers, and legumes. Although beef cattle and sheep may get much of their food from range land not suitable for cultivation, they also consume considerable amounts of grain and hay. Although dairy cattle, hogs, and chickens consume some food that would otherwise be wasted, they are fed largely from cultivated crops. Most of the arable land used to produce grain or hay for animals could be used to produce grain or tubers for human consumption. In converting hay or grain into milk, meat, or eggs, there is considerable loss. Only a fraction of the plant proteins and carbohydrates consumed by animals for growth and activity are converted into animal proteins and fats (12).

In order to compare diets in terms of the land needed for food production, the proportion of food from animal sources must be considered. The comparison is best made on the basis of " original calories," which include not only the grains and tubers used directly by man, but also the grain and hay fed to livestock to produce the meat, milk, and eggs. In the United States, more than 25 per cent of our food comes from animal sources; the average daily consumption of original calories is about 10,000 per capita. In Asia, less than 5 per cent of the food is in the form of meat, milk, eggs or fish; the daily consumption of original calories per capita is probably not more than 2500.

Although the rate of 10,000 original calories consumed per person per day in the United States is both unnecessary and wasteful, an adequate, palatable, and well-balanced diet does require at least 5000 to 6000 original calories. It is even possible to provide a diet adequate in proteins and carbohydrates based upon little more than 3000 original calories; but a people who have effected their Demographic Transition and enjoy reasonably high living standards will not be satisfied with a diet based largely upon beans, flour, peanuts, cabbage, and spinach, even if it is supplemented with a little milk and fortified with synthesized vitamins. Moreover, such a diet provides no insurance for lean years; a crop failure in any large area of the world would result in starvation for many people. With livestock farming, the animals plus the grain commonly used to feed the animals provide food reserves in case widespread floods or drought temporarily reduce yields. Livestock also promote soil improvement and a more permanent system of agriculture.

Because agriculture provides the foundation for our modern civilization, a brief history of its development may help to clarify the problems and possibilities of future food production. The earliest extensive agriculture was developed on the flood plains of the great rivers, where the soil could be cultivated without removing forests or breaking the heavy sod of the grasslands. Spring floods solved the problem of soil fertility, because each year the fertility of the land was replenished by new silt deposits. As populations grew, new land was needed; the farmer had to move to the grasslands and forested areas. The preparation and cultivation of such land demanded more labor, but with primitive tools and the aid of domestic animals it was done. Most of these upland soils could not be cropped for long without depleting the fertility of the soil — a fact that led to a shifting agriculture. In wooded areas the timber was burned and the land was cultivated for a few years; then the farmer moved on. Natural regeneration of the forests on worn-out farms eventually restored the fertility of the soil so that it could be used again. This wasteful method of farming is still used in many parts of Africa and Latin America. The grasslands were generally more fertile, but they also gradually declined in fertility, which could be restored by fallowing or, later, by soiling crops and manures.

Devices for restoring soil fertility by fallowing or resting the soil, or by growing " green manure " to replenish organic matter, were well known long before the advent of the cult of " organic gardening." In Roman times, Columella observed that " it is true that the ground after it was brought into cultivation, seems to fall back in the scale of fertility; but the fruitfulness which it first possessed was owing to its having been fattened, as it were, by the residue from so many former crops which it had spontaneously brought forth." The use of legumes to restore the fertility of worn-out soils is equally ancient. Cato observed that " there are some crops which tend to nourish the earth; thus for instance, corn [wheat] land is manured by the lupine, the bean, and the vetch." The value of both mineral and organic fertilizers was also known in Roman times; Virgil commented:

> Yet sprinkle sordid ashes all around
> And load with fattening dung thy fallow ground.

The problems of farming were also poetically documented in Virgil's lament:

Yet even upon the grain fell plague, erelong
Mildew defiled the stalks, and everywhere
The barbed thistles gathered in lawless throng
Till villainous weeds displaced the harvest there.

Soil erosion, also an ancient problem, was observed by Plato (75):

At the period, however, with which we are dealing, when Attica was still intact, what are now her mountains were lofty, soil-clad hills; her so-called shingle plains of the present day were full of rich soil; and her mountains were heavily af-forested — a fact of which there are still visible traces. There are mountains in Attica which can now keep nothing but bees, but which were clothed, not so very long ago, with fine trees producing timber suitable for roofing the largest buildings; the roofs hewn from this timber are still in existence. There were also many lofty cultivated trees, while the country produced boundless pasture for cattle. The annual supply of rainfall was not lost, as it is at present, through being allowed to flow over the denuded surface to the sea, but was received by the country, in all its abundance, into her bosom, where she stored it in her impervious potter's earth and so was able to discharge the drainage of the heights into the hollows in the form of springs and rivers with an abundant volume and a wide ter-ritorial distribution.

The present deplorable condition of the land of Greece is well known (121).

The techniques and trials of ancient farming continued with little change until the eighteenth century. There was some improvement in both farm practices and farm equipment during the eighteenth century and the first half of the nineteenth. But modern agriculture began with the development of mineral fertilizers, the control of insect pests and fungus diseases, the introduction of ef-ficient farm machinery and improved varieties of farm crops — all within the past century and largely during the past fifty years.

Since the discovery of the role of mineral fertilizers in crop production, their use has increased steadily.* The use of mineral fertilizers was largely responsible for the doubling of crop production in Germany between 1880 and 1910; France, still relying on farm manure, increased yields very little during the same period. Much of the high agricultural production of the countries of Western Europe and of Japan can be attributed to the liberal use of mineral fertilizers; farmers of these countries use far more fertilizers per acre than farmers in the United States (19).

The development of new fungicides has progressed considerably since the discovery that Bordeaux mixture would control certain plant diseases. The new organic sprays are not only more effective but easier to apply. Even greater progress has been made in the control of insect pests, although some of the insecticides are so toxic that they must be used with care to protect both operators and consumers. In most of the world, crop plants get little or no protection from insect pests or plant diseases.

Since 1700, there has been continual improvement in farm machinery. But the development of power equipment during the past few decades has greatly increased farm-labor efficiency and has made possible the preparation of new arable land at moderate costs.

* In 1948–49 the world used more than 3 million tons of commercial nitrogen, over 5 million tons of phosphoric acid, and well over 3 million tons of potash — most of it in Europe and North America.

The recent development of modern farm machinery and motor-driven equipment has greatly increased the farmer's productivity. In Asia, where small farms are still cultivated with primitive equipment, operated by human energy or by domestic animals, about 75 per cent of the working population must engage in farming in order to provide the entire population with less than 2500 original calories per day per capita. In the United States, 15 per cent of the working population can produce more than 10,000 original calories per capita per day for our entire population. The average American farmer produces more than ten times as much food as the Chinese or Indian farmer — and does it with the expenditure of much less time and sweat.

The introduction of crops from one land to another has played an important part in world agriculture. The Old World has provided wheat, soybeans, sugar cane, and numerous fruits, legumes, and grasses. The New World has provided potatoes, corn, and sweet potatoes — crops now of great value to Old World agriculture. There are still opportunities for introducing new and valuable varieties of food plants into many parts of the world.

The improvement of crop varieties by selection and plant breeding has also contributed much to agricultural production in most countries. Most of the crop varieties now grown in Western countries are the product of agricultural science. By breeding and selection it has been possible to achieve higher yields, greater resistance to disease and drought, greater uniformity in size and time of maturity, and often better quality. According to K. S. Quisenberry (85), the newer wheat varieties developed in the United States have produced about 170 million bushels per year more than would have been possible with the varieties grown twenty-five years ago. Plant breeders have produced varieties of wheat with stiffer straw for combine harvesting; earlier-maturing varieties, which permit a northern extension of the wheat belt; drought-resistant varieties, which make possible the growth of wheat in areas of low rainfall; and disease-resistant wheats, which defy rust, blight and smut.

One of the greatest contributions to higher yields has been the utilization of hybrid vigor.* Jenkins (57) estimates that hybrid corn has increased yields at least 30 per cent on the land where it has been grown. The use of hybrid corn in this country has produced annually about 500 million bushels more during recent years than would have been possible with the old open-pollinated varieties. Hybrid vigor is now being utilized in some other crops and even in livestock and poultry. This frontier of science could be expanded considerably.

Advances in plant breeding, extended use of fertilizers, and better control of insect pests and plant diseases have increased yields in many countries. But there has been little increase in the yields per acre of major crops in most of the world during the past forty years. The trends of yields per acre of the bread grains (wheat and rye) and the coarse grains (corn, barley, and oats) grown largely for livestock food are shown in Figure 7. There was not much increase in the yields per acre of these two major

* The development of the idea, and its practical utilization, originated at Princeton and at Harvard.

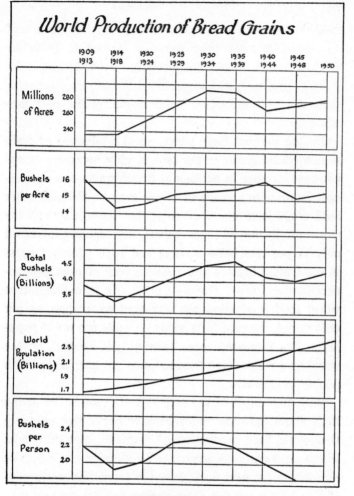

FIGURE 7

WORLD PRODUCTION OF BREAD GRAINS

In certain countries new agricultural techniques, better crop varieties, and a more liberal use of fertilizers have increased yields per acre. However, for the world as a whole there has been little increase in yields per acre, because of soil erosion, poor farm practices, and use of marginal land. Although considerable new land has been brought into cultivation, the production of food in most of the world during the past two decades has not kept pace with population growth.

(Data from the Food and Agricultural Organization of the United Nations.)

crops grown in the United States from 1880 to 1940.* The increase since 1940 was due in part to favorable weather; but an important factor has been the high price of farm products, which permitted the farmers to double their use of commercial fertilizer during the past decade (36).

During the past forty years, world production of grain has increased about 10 per cent, largely because of a 15-per-cent increase in acreage of bread grains and a 5-per-cent increase in acreage of coarse grains. Perhaps other food crops have increased somewhat more, although the world production of sugar, tubers, and legumes increased only 11 per cent between 1934 and 1938 (drought years in the United States) and 1948 (a year of peak production in the United States) (113). It is unlikely that world food production has increased more than 15 per cent during the past forty years — while the world population has increased more than 30 per cent. For the world as a whole, food production is not keeping up with population growth.

With two-thirds of the present world population living little above subsistence levels, it is imperative not only that world food production be increased, but that it be increased very considerably. To provide an *adequate* diet within the next decade for the expanding world population would involve literally doubling the present rate

* Wheat yields remained at about 13 bushels per acre and corn yields at about 26 bushels per acre, except for a decline in the drought years during the 1930's. During the past decade, the yields of wheat have increased to about 19 bushels per acre and corn to about 33 bushels per acre; the peak production in 1948 was over 40 bushels per acre. Average yields per acre of all crops during the past fifteen years have increased about 30 or 40 per cent.

of world food production. There are two major ways of
setting about any such task — to increase the yields per
acre of land now in cultivation or to make new land productive. Because most of the best arable land of the
world is already in cultivation and because it is possible
to increase yields per acre very substantially, the first of
these possibilities seems to be the more practical.

TABLE 3

ESTIMATES OF THE WORLD'S ARABLE LAND
(in billions of acres)

	Now cultivated	Potentially arable	Total arable
International Institute of Agriculture (1941–46)	1.4	....	....
Pearson and Harper (78)	1.5	1.1	2.6
F.A.O. Yearbook 1950	2.8	0.9	3.7
R. M. Salter (97)	1.9	1.3	3.7
O. E. Baker (4)	2.4	2.7	5.1
C. B. Fawcett (34)	3.1	7.8	10.9
H. L. Shantz (128)	....	....	15.7
Dept. of State (O.C.L.)	2.4	....	....

How much more food could be produced on the land
now cultivated throughout the world? The question is
difficult to answer with precision because of the great
variations in soil and climate. We do not even know how
much land is now actually cultivated in the world; recent
estimates, as shown in Table 3, vary from 1.4 to 3.1 billion acres. Actually these discrepancies are not as great
as they first appear: the lower estimates are based upon
land that produces a harvested crop, and the more liberal
estimates include fallow land and plowable pasture. It
is probable that not more than 2 to 2.4 billion acres are

actually cultivated — approximately 1 acre per person for the present world population. Because soils and climates are so variable, a brief survey of present and potential production per acre in various parts of the world should provide a better estimate for future food production.

In the United States about 2.4 acres per person are used to provide our rather liberal diet of more than 10,000 original calories per person per day. In many countries of Western Europe an acre of cultivated land per person supplies an adequate diet of about 6000 original calories; a fertile soil, an equable climate, the liberal use of fertilizer, and proper crop rotation have enabled the European farmers to increase the production of the soil and maintain high yields. In Japan the farmers can provide food for one person on about a quarter of an acre of land, the dietary standard being about half that of Western Europe; with intensive labor, liberal use of fertilizer, and often the production of two crops per year, the Japanese farmer produces nearly twice as much food per acre as the European farmer. In order to provide a person with a good European diet it would require at present levels of production, an average of about 1.5 acres in North America, 1 acre in Europe, and half an acre in Japan.

In parts of the world it should be possible to increase yields substantially without excessive use of labor and capital. The utilization of better crop varieties, more fertilizer, crop rotation, and better control of the insect pests and plant diseases could increase yields perhaps as much as 50 per cent in North America, the U.S.S.R., and South America. The farms in much of Asia are already intensely cultivated and production is relatively high; but considerable increase in yields could be attained without diminishing returns, especially in India. Greater yields could be produced in Europe, but probably with rapidly diminishing returns for the capital and labor expended. For the world as a whole, Robert M. Salter (97) has estimated that yields per acre could be increased 30 per cent in the near future. Even if yields could be increased 50 per cent, the world's food supply would hardly provide an adequate diet for the present population, assuming a uniform distribution of the world's food and Western European dietary levels for all.

If the world's growing population is to be adequately fed, new land must eventually be brought into cultivation. Estimates of the amount of new land suitable for this purpose are even more variable than estimates of land now in cultivation (Table 3). If the potentially arable land is limited to areas of good soil, adequate and well-distributed rainfall, favorable topography, and a sufficiently long growing season, little new land can be cultivated profitably. If, on the other hand, we include all land that can be turned over with a plow after clearing the forests and draining the swamps (regardless of soil fertility, temperatures, or rainfall), the potentially arable land might well approach 10 or 12 billion acres. However, only at great cost for clearing forests, drainage, irrigation, and soil improvement can even one billion acres of new land be brought into cultivation.

The problem is not simply how much more land might be brought into cultivation — but how much might be so utilized without excessive costs of labor and capital. Much of the new land that could be cultivated comes under the same category as the abandoned farmland of New England. Since 1800, nearly 10 million acres of New England land once in cultivation or used as pasture have been abandoned because they were no longer profitable to farm (10). If necessary, this land could be brought back into cultivation after clearing the second-growth forests. But high yields would be possible only with excessive expenditures for soil improvement, liberal applications of mineral fertilizer, and supplementary irrigation systems.

Perhaps the greatest over-all need for an improved agriculture is soil conservation. Europe has maintained an efficient and permanent agriculture by proper crop rotation, the use of livestock, and the use of mineral fertilizers; the absence of serious soil erosion or decline in soil productivity has been aided by a favorable climate without torrential rains or high summer temperatures. In most of the world, soil erosion and the depletion of soil fertility are serious problems. According to H. H. Bennett, former chief of the U.S. Soil Conservation Service, soil erosion has essentially destroyed much range and crop land in many parts of the world (9):

Everywhere in the world natural resources have been depleted by ignorant and reckless exploitation that has ignored the inexorable natural laws which maintain them. . . . Throughout the world steadily increasing populations have put an ever-increasing strain on the dwindling resources. These two forces, each of which reinforces the other, have now brought mankind to an almost critical point.

Much of the marginal land now in cultivation should be returned to grass or forests. In order to keep marginal

land out of cultivation, it is essential to increase crop
production on the better land. This can be done by
proper crop rotation and efficient farm practices. The
use of legumes or grass to build up the organic matter of
the soil, plus adequate application of mineral fertilizers,
will result in higher yields of the cultivated crops. Livestock, which consume the cultivated grass and utilize pasture areas unsuited for crops, provide manures to contribute to the organic matter and fertility of the soil. In
terms of original calories, animals produce expensive food
in the form of meat and milk; but they are able to convert
grass into human food — and grass is essential in an efficient and permanent agriculture. The usual excuse for
growing cultivated crops year after year is that all of the
land is needed for the production of cash crops and food
for domestic consumption. But if the production of cultivated crops can be substantially increased by the use of
grass or legume rotation, manure, and commercial fertilizer, the farmer can grow just as much corn, cotton, or
potatoes on less land — and at the same time build up
his soil.

But new land, higher yields, and soil conservation offer
no solution to our general problem if living standards are
maintained at or reduced to subsistence levels. Firman
Bear, past president of the American Agronomy Society,
assures us that the United States could feed a population
of a billion people (8); but he has to assume enormous
irrigation projects, with water distilled or processed from
the ocean, the use of tremendous amounts of lime and
fertilizer, vast flood control measures and drainage projects. With all these expenditures, food costs would be

high; we would have to eat less meat and more potatoes and bread; and many of us would go to bed hungry every night — as do millions of people in other parts of the world today. Not only would food become scarce and expensive, but industry and education would suffer, until eventually most of the population would ironically be engaged in " modern " but subsistence farming. It would be unfortunate if greater agricultural production in the United States led only to a much larger population living at subsistence levels — as is true in most of the world.

The chief problem of agricultural production is not to grow the maximum amount of food at any cost, but to produce adequate food without excessive costs of labor and capital. If most of the capital and manpower of the world were devoted to the production of food, modern man would be little better off than his ancestors, who spent most of their time in hunting for their next meal. It is possible to process sea water so that it can be used to irrigate arid lands; but the costs of desalting, pumping, and moving the water are excessive. Much marginal land could be cleared, drained, or irrigated, and enriched with organic and mineral fertilizers; but if the expenditure of capital and labor increased food prices so greatly that the average man had to spend more than half of his income for food, the living standards would decline to dangerously low levels.

Agriculture must do more than provide food. It must do this so efficiently that at least half of the population is released for work in industry, distribution, communication, education, and the arts and sciences, with reasonably high living standards for all.

The problem of providing adequate food for all of the world's people is made even more difficult by the fact that the ratio between potential agricultural resources and populations varies greatly in the major areas of the world. Normally, most of the world's food production is consumed in the country in which it is raised. In a few countries a high degree of industrialization permits expenditures for substantial food imports. But industrial monopolies and colonial empires are not likely to survive, and most countries must be largely dependent upon their own agricultural resources. To adopt a point made by John D. Black, professor of agricultural economics at Harvard University (10), the world's people cannot be compared to a drove of hogs feeding from a common trough. Even if one country is able to produce large food surpluses, it is not likely to send great quantities of food to countries which have nothing to export in return.

The complexity of this situation is well illustrated by the estimates of the Food and Agriculture Organization of the United Nations (Table 4). The estimates of potentially arable land are not precise; but for the more critical areas they are adequate to allow the drawing of general conclusions. The table indicates that most of the continental areas have enough cultivated or potentially arable land to provide adequate diets for present populations and for some population growth. North America and Oceania have enough potentially arable land to feed considerably larger populations. The estimates of potentially arable land in the U.S.S.R., Africa, and South America are incomplete and are probably too low; but the problems of efficient land use may not permit adequate diets for much larger populations in those areas. Without industrial monopolies and colonial empires, Europe will do well to provide high living standards for present populations. The most critical area is Asia, which contains more than half of the world's population. With great effort, Asia might be able to provide adequate

TABLE 4

THE WORLD'S DISTRIBUTION OF LAND AND PEOPLE

	1950 population (millions)	Cultivated acres (millions)	Present acres per person	Total arable acres (millions)	Potential acres per person
Asia	1,272	787	.6	1,014	.8
U.S.S.R.	200	556	2.8	586	2.9
Europe	394	363	.9	388	1.0
Africa	199	458	2.3	655	3.3
North America	166	595	3.6	859	5.2
Latin America	162	158	1.0	321	2.0
Oceania	13	47	3.6	77	6.0
World	2,406	2,838	1.2	3,774	1.5

Data from F.A.O. Yearbook, 1950. The figures in the last column are based on 1950 population.

diets for its present population of nearly 1300 million people with less than an acre of land per capita.

The greatest needs in developing the agriculture of Asia are fertilizers, farm machinery, insecticides, and fungicides.* A greater use of fertilizer, more efficient farm tools, and the use of modern insecticides could increase crop production in much of Asia. In order to increase farm-labor efficiency, the size of the farms must

* At present nearly 90 per cent of the mineral fertilizers consumed throughout the world are used by the countries of Western Europe, North America, and Oceania. These same countries have 83 per cent of the world's tractors (128). They consume nearly all of the fungicides and insecticides.

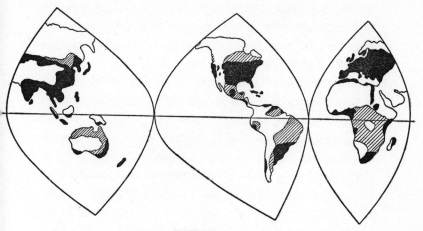

FIGURE 8

THE ARABLE LAND OF THE WORLD

The cultivated land of the world (shown in BLACK) totals about 2,400 million acres — or about 1 acre per person for the present world population. The potentially arable land not now cultivated (indicated by DIAGONAL LINES) may equal the acreage now in cultivation. However, much of this land is of poor quality, or lies in areas of low rainfall or short growing seasons. Much of it could be brought into cultivation only at excessive costs for clearing, irrigation systems, and prevention of soil erosion. Little new land can be brought into cultivation where population density is high, as in Europe and Asia.

In most of the world, yields per acre could be increased substantially. But food production in most of the world would have to be doubled to provide adequate diets even for the present population. In much of the world, orthodox agriculture cannot provide adequate food for much larger populations.

The areas shown on the map are very roughly indicated. (They are based upon estimates made by H. H. Bennett, former chief of the United States Soil Conservation Service.)

be increased, but other occupations must be available for the displaced farm labor. Any rehabilitation program must be a balanced one, with a proper integration of agriculture, industry, and education.

The problems of agricultural improvement are difficult in any country that has an illiterate population, limited capital resources, and inadequate land. But the greatest problem is the population growth during the Demographic Transition. In most of these countries food production will have to be doubled to provide adequate diets and other necessities for the present population. With an annual increase of population of only 1 per cent, the production would have to be doubled again in 70 years. With population growth at 2 per cent annually, the food resources would have to be doubled every 35 years. How long such population growth would continue is difficult to predict; but judging from the experience of some of the countries of Western Europe and of Japan, one could expect a minimum of a threefold increase in population before the completion of the Demographic Transition. Including the initial increase needed to raise dietary levels of present populations to reasonable requirements, the ultimate food supply in Asia would have to increase at least 500 per cent above present levels if populations increased threefold. Orthodox agriculture cannot meet such needs.

Most of the best agricultural land of the world is already cultivated. Those who see possibilities for a great increase in the world's cultivated land inevitably turn to the tropics. Robert M. Salter (97) has estimated that a

billion acres of new land in the tropical areas of South
America and Africa could be brought into cultivation, and
that this land would yield nearly twice as much per acre
as the land now cultivated in the temperate zone. He
has estimated that, by increasing 30 per cent the yields of
the 1.9 billion acres now in cultivation, and by bringing
into cultivation 300 million more acres of land in the
north temperate zone and 1000 million acres of tropical
land, enough food could be produced by 1960 to more
than meet world needs.

But those who are most familiar with tropical agriculture have grave doubts about the productivity of tropical
soils. Robert Pendleton, professor of tropical soils and
agriculture at Johns Hopkins University, has said, in a
personal communication: ". . . except for relatively very
small areas of soils from volcanic ash and recent alluvial
soils, most of the soils of the tropics, judged by temperate
zone standards, are extremely low in plant nutrient sub-
stances and organic matter." L. Dudley Stamp, professor
of social geography at the London School of Economics,
is probably as well acquainted with the problems of tropical land use as any one in the world. In commenting on
the use of equatorial forest lands for agriculture he concludes: " By and large, if cleared, the equatorial forests
would produce vast areas of poor or indifferent soil, liable
to become still further impoverished, and further liable to
marked soil erosion. The old myth that equatorial soils
are of great fertility dies hard " (107).

The tropical savannas offer greater possibilities for an
expanding agriculture. But the long dry seasons, and the
excessive water in the rainy seasons, present difficult

obstacles. The rapid loss of organic matter and the excessive leaching of soil nutrients are not the only problems
of tropical agriculture; high and relatively uniform temperatures throughout the year are not conducive to human
effort (37).

There is no possibility that either the proposed increase
in yields or the use of greater world acreage will be attained in the near future (61). Even if these goals could
be reached, population growth would soon nullify all
gains in food production. In commenting on Salter's
estimates, Professor Black makes the following analysis (10):

Even with all this new land cleared and developed and
farmed according to modern practices, the increased supply of
meats and pulses would already have been exhausted by 1960,
and if the population increased at the same rate after 1960 as
assumed for the years 1935–1960, the increased milk supply
would be exhausted by 1970, and the increased supply of
fruits and vegetables by 1980. After that, any population
growth would be possible only by reducing the per-capita intake of milk and meat and living more on cereals, roots and
tubers, sugar and vegetable oils. Even with diets shifted to
cereals and roots and tubers, the food supply would reach its
limit within 75 years.

If anyone wants to take exception to Salter's estimates and
say they are not liberal enough, let him double them. The
result will be the same, except that it will be deferred.

It should now be clear that the two lines of action proposed . . . increasing food production, and increasing the
power to buy food, will not be enough — that adjustments of
population to resources is also necessary. Indeed, this is by
far the largest part of the problem.

The land is not the only source of food. It has been
shown that most of the organic matter produced by

photosynthesis each year is produced in the oceans. Yet the annual harvest of marine fish is only about 20 million tons, of which only 5 or 6 millions are used for food (128). Fish provide a substantial part of the diet in a few countries, but for the world as a whole the average annual consumption is only about five pounds per capita. The production of marine fish could probably not be increased more than 50 per cent without jeopardizing future supplies.

With the great photosynthetic activity in the oceans of the world, why is the yield of fish so limited? This apparent paradox has been explained by Clark (20). The conversion of grass and grain into meat involves one conversion cycle, which results in a return of only about 10 per cent of the original plant proteins and carbohydrates in the form of animal proteins and fats. However, the production of edible fish involves *several* conversion cycles. The algae of the ocean, which provide all of the original food supply, are eaten by the minute marine animals, the zooplankton. These in turn are eaten by larger animals, chiefly the small crustacea. The crustacea are eaten by the smaller fish, which in turn are eaten by the larger fish. If marine animals are no more efficient than land animals in converting food from one form to another, each conversion cycle results in a net return of only 10 per cent. Four conversion cycles would return only 0.1 per cent of the original food value of the algae. Weiss (125) has estimated that it requires 100,000 pounds of marine algae to produce a pound of codfish.

It is possible to avoid the multiple-conversion cycle in marine food production by harvesting the plant and animal plankton directly from the ocean, by screening out these minute organisms. These plankton are nutritious and palatable — although, if consumed in large amounts, they may have deleterious effects. The cost of harvesting them from the ocean would be exorbitant, because the yield, even in favorable areas, is only about one cubic centimeter per cubic meter of sea water, or one part of plankton per million of sea water. At best, the oceans of the world can provide only a small fraction of the food needed by even the present population of the world.

From this general survey, we can draw certain conclusions. The arable land of the world, if properly developed, could provide adequate diets for larger populations in much of the world. But unfortunately the greatest needs for more food are in areas already densely populated and with rapid, or potentially rapid, population growth. The most critical area is Asia, with less than an acre of potentially arable land per capita for the present population. The potential population growth in Africa and Latin America could also absorb any increased food supply, without any significant increase in living standards.

Plans for adequate world food production must reckon with the formidable fact that by the end of another decade there will probably be about 300 million more people to feed. Orthodox agriculture cannot provide adequate food and reasonable living standards for all of the world's people — unless birth rates in most of the world are soon reduced to little more than replacement levels.

5
Energy and Minerals: Consumption and Reserves

Primitive man had to depend almost solely upon human labor to meet his energy needs: to obtain his food, make his clothes, and provide transportation. Although he obtained some energy by burning wood to heat his hut and cook his meals, practically all productive energy was provided by human labor. The productive energy of an active adult is about 150 " energy units " per year — equivalent to 150 kilowatt-hours of electrical energy, or enough to run a one-horsepower motor about 187 hours; if one takes into account the young, the aged and the infirm, the average annual output of productive human energy is about 100 units (118). Human energy alone, even under favorable conditions, can provide little more than a subsistence level of existence.

The domestication of animals considerably increased man's source of energy. One of the larger draft animals, such as horses, cattle, and camels, can produce about 600 units of productive energy each year. Under favorable conditions, and with ample arable land, draft animals can increase man's energy resources fivefold to tenfold. In the United States a hundred years ago, manpower provided about 15 per cent of the energy used for productive purposes, while draft animals provided about 80 per cent (44).

In densely populated areas, however, draft animals contribute relatively little energy for agriculture and

TABLE 5

SOURCE AND USE OF ENERGY PER CAPITA (1948)
(in kilowatt-hours of electricity equivalent per year)

	Source of energy			Use of inanimate energy		
	Man	Animal	Inanimate	Industry	Transport	Domestic (including agriculture)
North America	100	40	13,790	6,300	3,600	4,000
Oceania	100	70	3,520	1,200	1,300	1,000
Europe	100	30	3,136	1,600	500	1,000
U.S.S.R.	100	45	3,168	1,300	700	1,100
Latin America	100	120	2,640	1,000	800	800
Asia	100	45	384	150	80	160
Africa	100	30	656	90	200	350
World	100	40	2,160	1,000	500	700

Data on human and animal energy from Department of State (118), with corrections for draft animals in 1948; on inanimate energy from Woytinsky (128). Use of inanimate energy in 1948 based upon proportions estimated for 1937 by Department of State (118). For some areas the data are little more than estimates; but they are adequate for comparative purposes.

transportation because most of the land is needed for growing food for man. In Asia, draft animals supply only half as much productive energy as man does, and in Africa only a third as much (Table 5). Yet agriculture in these areas is almost completely dependent upon human and animal labor. Nearly three-quarters of the working population in Asia and Africa are engaged in farming; yet the dietary levels are very low.

With the introduction of power machinery, agricultural efficiency was greatly increased. The farm tractor will produce in a year about 4000 units of energy, compared with about 600 produced by a horse and 150 produced by a man (118).* In the United States tractors and other power equipment now provide most of the energy for tilling the fields and harvesting the crops. With the aid of power machinery and modern farm practices, only a sixth of the labor force can provide ample food for all (128). Power machinery also releases crop land formerly needed to grow hay and grain for the horses and mules. According to the United States Department of Agriculture (116), about a sixth of our farmland has been released for food production during the past thirty years by the decrease in the number of horses and mules. *The release of 70 million acres formerly used to produce food for draft animals has been an important factor in providing ample food for the 50 million people added to our population between 1920 and 1953.* If our agriculture were still powered only by human and animal labor, it is very doubtful that we would have surplus food and ample diets in this country today.

Man and his domestic animals could not possibly provide the enormous amounts of energy required by an industrial culture. Although energy from inanimate sources has greatly increased the efficiency of agriculture, most of the energy produced by coal, oil, gas, and water power

* In 1951 there were more than 6 million tractors in the world, but more than 4 million of them were in North America, nearly a million in Europe, and about half a million in the U.S.S.R.; the rest of the world had less than half a million (128).

is used for industry and transportation. The amount of energy provided by man and his domestic animals does not vary greatly in different parts of the world, but there are enormous differences in the consumption of inanimate energy.

The per-capita consumption of energy from coal, petroleum, natural gas, wood, and hydroelectric power ranges from nearly 14,000 units in North America to less than 400 units in Asia.* The average person in the United States and Canada has the equivalent of nearly a hundred slaves to help produce his food, build his house, supply his clothes, transportation, and means of communication, and to heat and light his house and place of work. The family automobile alone uses about 5000 energy units per year — more than that produced by 30 men.

The per-capita consumption of inanimate energy in 1948 in Oceania, Europe, and the U.S.R.R. was 3000 to to 3500 units — about a fourth as much as in North America. Energy consumption varied greatly among the countries of Europe, with a per-capita consumption of nearly 8000 units in the United Kingdom to only 400 in Greece. Latin American countries averaged about 2600 energy units per capita; but here too there was a great variation among countries. The per-capita consumption in Asia and Africa was less than 400 units, if allowance is made for the wasteful burning of wood in Africa. Here too there is considerable variation in different coun-

* With less than 7 per cent of the world population, North America uses more than 40 per cent of the world's production of inanimate energy — 40 per cent of the coal, 66 per cent of the petroleum, and 40 per cent of the hydroelectric power (128).

tries, from a consumption of about 1300 units in Japan to less than 40 in Thailand, and from more than 3000 in the Union of South Africa to almost none in Nigeria (other than that obtained from wood).

The development of a modern industrial culture requires a minimum per-capita consumption of inanimate energy of the order of 3000 units. A country rich in agricultural resources could provide reasonably good living standards with no more than 2000 units per capita — as Ireland does. But most of the countries of Western Europe consume 3000 to 5000 units per capita. In England, where about half of the food is imported, a per-capita energy consumption of nearly 8000 units is required to maintain the present living standards.

In many countries of Europe and most of the countries of Latin America, the per-capita energy consumption should be doubled, and in practically all of Asia and Africa it should be increased about tenfold, in order to provide the industrial and agricultural production needed for adequate living standards in a modern world. Furthermore, it will be necessary to provide additional energy resources for the inevitable increase of population.

Can present resources provide the energy needs of a modern world? Today the sources of inanimate energy are coal, petroleum, natural gas, water power, and wood. The fossil fuels now provide more than 90 per cent of all energy used for productive purposes. Wood is an important source of energy in much of the world, primarily for space heating and for cooking, but it is a negligible factor in the production of power for industry and transportation.

In 1950 coal provided more than half of the energy consumed in the world and more than 90 per cent of the coal was used in Europe, North America, and the U.S.S.R. (63). It was not by accident that Europe and North America have become highly industrialized and

TABLE 6

THE WORLD'S COAL RESOURCES

	1937 consumption		Reserves		Duration of supply (in years)	
	Tons (billions)	Percent of total	Tons (billions)	Percent of total	At 1937 rate	At U.S. per-capita rate
North America	.462	34	2840	51	3000	3000
Europe	.636	45	620	11	500	200
U.S.S.R.	.114	8	1525	27	6000	1000
Asia	.118	9	297	5	1300	40
Africa	.022	2	222	4	5000	200
Latin America	.010	1	36	1	1800	40
Oceania	.015	1	34	1	1000	500
World	1.379	100	5574	100	2000	400

Data from Department of State (118).

that the U.S.S.R. is industrializing rapidly. Coal has been the primary source of energy for industry, and most of the world's coal deposits are in the Northern Hemisphere (Table 6). If Latin America, Africa, and much of Asia are to develop industrially, they must look to sources other than coal for their fuel and power.

As shown in Table 6, the reserves of coal in most of the Northern Hemisphere would seem to be adequate for thousands of years. If all of the world's reserves could be recovered and converted into energy to be utilized by all of the world, these reserves would last about 2000 years, at the 1937 rate of consumption. If, however, the rest of the world consumed coal at the same rate per capita as the United States now does, the reserves would last less than four hundred years, even with no increase in population. The world population may well increase at least twofold in less than one hundred years, thus doubling the energy needs of the world.

Moreover it is possible that the amount of coal that can be recovered without excessive cost may be considerably less than assumed. Estimating the world reserves of coal that can be recovered at less than twice the present costs, P. C. Putnam (84b) arrives at a figure of about 2 trillion tons. Since much or most of the world's coal will soon have to be converted into liquid fuel, with a conversion loss of energy of about 50 per cent, the effective coal reserves would provide the energy equivalent of only about 1 trillion tons for the entire world, and only 150 million tons for the United States.

On the basis of even the most optimistic estimates, world coal reserves would provide the needed energy for a highly industrialized world for only a few hundred years. And, if both population and per-capita consumption of energy continue to increase at present rates, the demands for energy would be increased at least twentyfold by the year 2050. The world's reserves of coal cannot possibly meet the demands for energy in the relatively near future.

Petroleum is the second-most-important source of energy in the world today. Its rate of consumption is increasing rapidly; and most of the petroleum is used by the same countries that use most of the world's coal.* Although nearly a third of the consumption in the United States in 1950 was used for heat, petroleum is used largely for transportation. Modern transportation uses enormous amounts of energy. The 50 million automobiles in the United States use energy, from gasoline, equivalent to 250 billion kilowatt-hours of electricity each year — nearly 10 per cent of all the inanimate energy consumed annually in the United States. A heavy transport airplane may use more than a million energy units annually.

Estimates of the world's reserves of petroleum have been notoriously unreliable. The visible reserves of 1937 were estimated at about 50 billion barrels (118). Later a more "optimistic" estimate put visible reserves at 92 billion barrels — or little more than twenty times the annual consumption. Probable reserves are much more liberal — 610 billion barrels according to Ayres (3). Levorsen (66) estimates that 500 billion barrels of petroleum might be found beneath land areas, and perhaps 1000 billion barrels beneath the continental shelves. These estimated 1500 billion barrels — assuming that they could all be recovered — would satisfy the present rate of world consumption for nearly 400 years. However, if all the world's 2400 million people used as much petroleum per capita as we in the United States did in 1950, the reserves would last less than 40 years. In any case, the probability is that the amount of reserves actually recoverable will be considerably less than 1500 bil-

* In 1950 the world consumption of petroleum was about 4 billion barrels. By 1975 the demand may well exceed 10 billion barrels, if available (3). In 1937 North America consumed 60 per cent of the world production of petroleum, Europe 15 per cent, and the U.S.S.R. 9 per cent.

lion barrels.   E. W. Pehrson, chief of the Economics and
Statistical Division of the U.S. Bureau of Mines, has
estimated that the world's petroleum reserves would last
for 160 years at current rates of consumption — but
only 18 years if the world per-capita consumption equaled
that of this country (79).

Liquid fuel can be derived from sources other than petroleum. As petroleum reserves are depleted, these other
sources must be utilized more extensively. The oil shales
might produce as much as 600 million barrels of oil (3).
Oil can also be made from coal by various processes.

The world's petroleum deposits are more evenly distributed than the world's coal deposits.* Petroleum may
also be transported more economically than coal, and even
now much petroleum is shipped over long distances. Yet
most petroleum is consumed by the same countries that
use most of the world's coal. This situation is likely to
continue, and the petroleum reserves of the industrially
undeveloped countries may be depleted before these countries have even begun their industrial evolution.

Water power is the only important source of energy
from *renewable* resources now exploited to contribute
energy for industrial use. Only about 6 per cent of the
world's potential water power has been developed, largely
in North America and Europe. About 6 per cent of the
energy requirements of the industrialized countries is
provided by hydroelectric power. In a few countries,

---

* North America has about 25 per cent of the known deposits, Europe
2 per cent, Russia 25 per cent, Latin America 13 per cent, Africa 1 per
cent, and Asia 34 per cent. Most of the petroleum in Asia is in the
Middle East and Indonesia.

such as Norway and Switzerland, water power provides most of the power for industry; but in general the countries that consume most of the world's hydroelectric power are the same ones that use most of the world's coal and petroleum (3).

The potential water power of the world, if fully developed, would provide nearly as much energy as the total present energy produced (about 4 trillion kilowatt-hours). Fortunately the areas that are deficient in coal reserves have most of the world's potential water power. Africa, for instance, although deficient in both coal and petroleum, has 40 per cent of the world's potential hydroelectric energy (118).

The estimates of the world's potential water-power resources are impressive until they are compared with total energy consumption in the industrialized nations, expressed in terms of energy per capita (in kilowatt-hours) as shown in Table 7. In terms of consumption, North America and Europe used in 1937 about 80 per cent of the world production of hydroelectric energy; and in 1950 the percentage was much higher. In terms of potential development, utilization of all the potential water known in North America would produce only 2200 kilowatt-hours per capita for the 1950 population — or only about 15 per cent of the total per-capita consumption of energy. For Europe the figure is about 30 per cent. Water power alone cannot possibly meet the major energy needs of North America, Europe, Australia, or most of Asia.

In the U.S.S.R. the full utilization of available water power could meet much of the needs of the present population, assuming that about 3000 energy units per capita would provide adequate power for essential industry and domestic use; but the U.S.S.R. could easily double her population before the end of this century. South America has even greater water resources per capita; but most of

TABLE 7

THE WORLD'S WATER–POWER RESOURCES
(in millions of kilowatt-hours equivalent)

	Hydroelectric energy				
	Production in 1937		Potential annual production		Total energy consumption
	Total	Per capita	Total	Per capita [1]	per capita 1948
North America	71,800	506	364,000	2,200	13,900
Oceania	1,560	156	34,000	260	3,700
Europe	64,100	164	361,500	900	3,300
U.S.S.R.	6,900	40	465,600	2,300	3,300
Latin America	4,870	38	539,000	3,550	2,800
Africa	540	4	1,615,900	8,080	800
Asia	22,750	20	557,600	440	500
World	172,558	82	3,938,100	1,640	1,676

[1] Based upon 1950 population (118).

this power is far from the present centers of population. Africa, with 40 per cent of the world's potential water power and less than 10 per cent of the world's population, could produce ample hydroelectric power in terms of total energy needs; but in Africa too the power would have to be transported over long distances to population centers at considerable cost and energy loss. In any case, hydroelectric power could not provide the energy needs for automobiles, trucks, and tractors, and could not readily meet all the needs of heavy industry.

In the industrially underdeveloped countries, wood provides most of the inanimate energy; but it is used largely for domestic purposes. Forests can provide little more than the needed timber and pulpwood for a modern world. Wood will not provide any significant amount of energy for transportation or industry.

It is evident that the capital reserves of energy — coal, petroleum, and natural gas — cannot long provide the enormous amounts of energy needed if the entire world is to develop an industry comparable to that in North America or even in Europe. Nor can the renewable sources of energy from wood, wind, and water power begin to meet modern demands. According to Putnam (84B) the consumption of mineral fuels has increased tenfold during the past hundred years, and the rate is increasing. Dr. Clifford C. Furnas, chemical engineer and chancellor of the University of Buffalo, predicted in a talk before the American Chemical Society in 1954 that the world consumption of energy may increase more than twentyfold during the next hundred years, if enough food can be provided for the expected threefold increase in world population by the year 2050 — and if the energy is available.

The peak of petroleum production will probably be reached before 1975, and by the year 2000 conversion of coal will probably supply most of the world's liquid fuel. By the year 2050 A.D. even the coal reserves may not be able to provide the needed fuel and power, unless more efficient means of recovery have been developed. At best the fossil fuels are not likely to provide the energy needs of the world for more than a few hundred years. New sources of energy must be developed in the relatively near future if our modern civilization is to survive. The possibilities of atomic and solar energy will be considered in the next chapter, " The New Frontiers of Science."

The capital reserves of the world not only are the source of our immediate energy consumption, but also provide great quantities of metals for our industrial civilization. In order to complete our present survey, we must take stock of the earth's mineral resources. Of the essential metals, iron ore is the most important and one of the most abundant; there are large deposits in both the Southern and Northern Hemispheres. Many other metals are essential in an industrial culture: without chromium, manganese, tungsten, and molybdenum, it would be impossible to produce steel alloys. Copper is essential for the electrical industry; and the demand for lead has been greatly increased. Without the mineral fertilizers — potash and phosphate rock — high crop yields could be maintained only by excessive labor. Sulphur plays an important part in the chemical industry in the production of mineral fertilizers, petroleum, rubber, paper, and many other products.

Many of these minerals are in short supply, and some are very limited in their distribution. The situation was well summarized by H. L. Keenleyside, speaking before the United Nations Scientific Congress (60):

It is clear that there is no serious and immediate overall and irreplaceable shortage of any essential mineral. But it is equally clear that the demand for mineral products is increasing at such a rate that unless there is a fundamental change in the economic fabric of human society, we will ultimately be faced with the exhaustion of many of our mineral resources. In some cases, particularly lead, copper and cobalt, and possibly iron and oil, the supply will be exhausted more rapidly than in others. New discoveries, improved methods of extraction and processing, and careful conservation will postpone the advent of critical mineral shortages. Substitution may provide alternate solutions . . . but this is a hope, not a promise.

TABLE 8

THE WORLD'S MINERAL RESOURCES
(number of years the known world supply will last)

	At current world rate of consumption	At current U.S. rate of consumption
Iron ore (*based on ultimate reserves*)	625	74
Manganese	250	50
Bauxite	200	31
Copper	45	5
Tin	38	6
Lead	33	4

Data from Pehrson's estimates (79).

E. W. Pehrson has presented estimates to show the imminent depletion of some of the more critical metals. Even if these estimates should prove to be unduly conservative, the fact that an expert in this field has come to such conclusions should give cause for general alarm. The figures for some of the more critical metals are shown in Table 8. Pehrson has estimated the number of years the supplies would last for the entire world, both at current world rate of consumption and at the projected rate of consumption if all of the world's people used as much of these metals per capita as we do in the United States.

The rapid exploitation of the world's capital reserves
has serious consequences for the United States in the
immediate future. Alan M. Bateman, chairman of the
geology department at Yale University, predicts that by
1975 we shall have to import much more of our mineral
and energy needs (7). (A partial list is shown in Table 9.)
This is true in spite of the fact that, with the exception
of the U.S.S.R., the United States is endowed with more
natural resources than any other major country. Not

TABLE 9

U.S. DEPENDENCE ON FOREIGN SOURCES OF MINERALS

	Imports (World War II)	Probable imports 1975
Sulphur	0	50%
Iron Ore	2.0%	35–40%
Bauxite (Aluminum)	18.2%	85%
Copper	37.6%	65%
Lead	44.2%	70%

Data from Bateman's estimates (7).

only are the energy and mineral demands of our industrial plants depleting our own resources; but also, if the
U.S. rate of demand continues to grow, we might deplete
the more critical reserves of the rest of the world even
before the underdeveloped areas begin their industrialization.

Any estimates of the world reserves of coal, oil, and
metals are approximations based upon incomplete surveys and upon the probable efficiency of recovery. For
instance, estimates of coal reserves in the United States
have been based upon the extraction of only 50 per cent

of the deposits. However, more efficient rates of extraction may be developed. Twenty years ago, only about 30 per cent of the oil in a deposit was recovered, but in recent years new techniques have permitted a recovery of as much as 70 per cent (129). In the case of minerals, the high-grade ores are mined first; but, as demands increase and extraction becomes more efficient, the low-grade ores can be used. We now use copper ore that contains only a tenth as much copper as the deposits used fifty years ago. In the United States more low-grade iron ore is being used as the high-grade ore is depleted. The utilization of low-grade ores makes available more of the mineral reserves, and the cost of extraction as the quality of the ore declines is often offset by more efficient methods.

There are, however, economic limitations to the extraction of minerals from low-grade deposits. We are assured that, because the earth's crust contains 5 per cent of iron, the world's iron resources are inexhaustible (94); but the " road to abundance " is not likely to be based upon the recovery of minerals at great depths in the earth's surface or by mining deposits of very low concentration. The granite mountains of New England contain 3 or 4 per cent of iron — but it is highly improbable that the ore can ever be extracted economically. Perhaps the geologist's estimates shown in Table 8 are too conservative; but they are far more realistic than are those of Rosin and Eastman, authors of *The Road to Abundance* (94).

The discovery of new reserves, more efficient methods of extraction and utilization, and careful conservation could substantially prolong the life of the world's capital reserves of energy and minerals. But if demands continue to increase at present rates, and if all of the world is to become industrialized, these capital reserves may last for only a few hundred years. If our present industrial civilization is to be more than a very brief episode in human history, the world's renewable or essentially inexhaustible resources must soon begin to supply our energy needs, and science must develop new sources of metals. Can the new frontiers of science meet these needs?

6

The New Frontiers of Science

The Demographic Transition of the modern Western nations was made possible in part by three essential factors: (a) the opening of new land frontiers; (b) the exploitation of capital resources; and (c) the application of scientific discoveries to agriculture and industry. Today, as we have seen, the first two of these elements no longer have unlimited possibilities of usefulness to mankind. We must therefore turn to the third of these factors. If the world is to free itself from poverty, malnutrition, illiteracy, and excessive population pressures, science will have to contribute even more in the future than it has in the past.

Here we shall discuss the new frontiers of science as they relate to the food supply, to sources of energy, and to the control of the birth rate.

As we have seen in Chapter 4, the first requirement for the success of the Demographic Transition is a more efficient food production, in order to provide an adequate diet for all and simultaneously to release part of the population for work in industry, government, and the arts. In most of the world (as we have seen), our present agricultural techniques might be able to double the production of food — but such an increase would provide no more than an adequate diet for present populations. If populations continue to grow at rapid rates, new techniques or new sources of food will have to be developed quickly.

Most of the basic scientific contributions to the art of agriculture are more than half a century old.* Great progress has been made in recent years in the development of power machinery, better insecticides and fungicides, and better mineral fertilizers; but these contributions are largely applications of scientific principles established long ago. Some important contributions have been made in the use of trace elements for soils deficient in essential minerals, the use of antibiotics in the nutrition of chickens and hogs, and the development of soil conditioners; but these discoveries have not yet been of major importance in increasing the world's food supply.

The recent development of soil conditioners by the chemical industry may be of considerable value in some parts of the world if the conditioners can be produced at reasonable costs. One of the greatest problems in agriculture is the maintenance of good soil texture to permit the absorption of water and air and to prevent hardening of the soil. A good soil texture can be achieved by the addition of organic matter in the form of manure or compost, or by the rotation of legumes and grasses with other crops. But in most areas of the world the organic mate-

* The benefits to plant growth that mineral fertilizers can provide were discovered 160 years ago, the laws of heredity nearly a hundred years ago, and the control of plant diseases 75 years ago. The only major contribution to the science of agriculture during this century was the theory of heterosis advanced by G. H. Shull in 1908 and its practical utilization by D. F. Jones in 1916.

rial is insufficient. A pound of the synthetic resin, Krilium, is said to be equivalent to the natural resins found in 100 to 1000 pounds of manure or compost. Although Krilium and other soil conditioners contain no plant nutrients, they do improve the texture of heavy soils. The limiting factor is their cost: at present prices the cost of treating an acre of land to a depth of six inches would amount to several thousand dollars.

The petroleum industry has recently produced a surfactant that promotes water movement in heavy soils, aiding aeration and improving soil drainage. The material is applied at the rate of only 15 to 50 pounds per acre. Further research may open other uses of surfactants in agriculture.

Only a few years ago it was found that antibiotics such as aureomycin, terramycin and penicillin, when fed to hogs and chickens, promoted more rapid growth in the young animals. There is also some evidence of stimulation of plant growth when certain antibiotics are added to the soil, or when trace elements are added at the rate of a few parts per million. Antibiotics in very dilute solutions appear to be of value in controlling systemic bacteria, and even certain fungus diseases of plants. The use of antibiotics in agriculture may be a significant factor in increasing food supplies in the near future (72).

Advances have also been made in the recent development of new insecticides, which have proved valuable not only in agriculture but even more in the control of insect-borne diseases of man. D.D.T., in helping to control fleas and mosquitoes, has been a major factor in the reduction of human death rates in many parts of the world. However, some of the new insecticides used in agriculture have so upset natural balances that the control of one insect pest stimulates the increase of others equally destructive. Others are so toxic that they must be handled with great care to avoid injury to man. Fortunately, some of the most recent organic phosphate insecticides are not only much less toxic to man but more nearly universal in their control of insects. Systemic insecticides that will kill any insect which feeds on plants may soon be available (58).

Complete utilization of known techniques in the improvement of soil fertility, control of plant and animal diseases, and development of better crop varieties and domestic animal breeds could provide adequate food for present populations in most of the countries that are not now able to produce adequate food. Orthodox agriculture cannot, however, provide adequate food for the people of Asia, and many smaller areas, if populations there continue for many decades to grow at present rates. New sources of food will have to be found if the needs of much larger populations are to be met.

Some years ago the British chemist J. D. Bernal proposed, as a solution of the food problem, a chemical synthesis of food from coal, limestone, and air. He contended that such a synthesis should make it possible to provide adequate food for thousands or even millions of times the present world population. However, he did not consider the fate of these thousands of billions of people when the coal reserves became exhausted.

More recently, Rosin and Eastman (94) have revived the idea of chemical synthesis of food, while mankind awaits the development of artificial photosynthesis. Unfortunately their references to the value of chemical weed control and soil conditioners are so absurd that a biologist is inclined to dismiss all their suggestions as science fiction. But it should be possible to synthesize carbohydrates, if cost is not a factor, and perhaps eventually to develop artificial photosynthesis. A new source of proteins is a more difficult problem, and the authors admit " that it would not be very convincing in the light of our present-day knowledge to say that synthetic proteins are destined to replace natural ones." Chemistry has made great contributions to agriculture and may eventually develop new sources of food — but for many decades, at least, the living plant must provide " our daily bread."

Food can be produced from other natural sources besides cultivated plants. Egon Glesinger, in his book *The Coming Age of Wood* (42) estimates that the 8 billion acres of forests in the world could supply both the food and the energy needed by the world's people. During World War II, wood was used in Sweden and Germany for wood-gas generators in motor vehicles and for the production of cellulose cattle feed. Wood can also be converted into wood sugar, which can in turn be converted into alcohol; or it can be used for growing edible yeasts rich in vitamins and proteins.

Although Glesinger's estimates are far too optimistic, and much remains to be done to develop efficient means of converting wood into food and motor fuel, forests represent great resources that are not now fully utilized. Most of the 5 billion acres now covered with virgin forests are probably of greater potential value for wood production than for agricultural crops. Not only should present forests be retained for wood production and water conservation, but hundreds of millions of acres should be reforested. Efficient restoration, harvesting, and utilization of our forest resources would provide much needed food and fuel and would help conserve both soil and water resources. A wood economy would not, however, contribute in a major way to the world's food supply. If newspapers over the world became as large as some of ours, most of the world's forests would be needed for lumber and wood pulp. It has been estimated that a single Sunday edition of the *New York Times* depletes 400 acres of forest land.

The most promising new source of food is the utilization of fungi and algae grown under controlled conditions. Yeast has long been used by man to produce alcohol from sugar by anaerobic fermentation. When yeast is added to a sugar solution, containing small amounts of nitrogen and phosphorus together with an adequate supply of air, it is possible to increase the yields of yeast without producing alcohol. By selection it is possible to grow yeasts that consist of as much as 50 per cent protein, and " fat yeasts " can produce up to 40 per cent fat. In addition to its fats and proteins, yeast is rich in vitamins. Because yeasts can be grown on molasses, in solutions of wood sugars, and on agricultural waste material, their costs are not excessive. Dried yeast, now selling at 10 to 20 cents per pound, is more expensive than comparable foods produced by agriculture, but its costs are not prohibitive (109). In many parts of the tropics, sugar cane will produce enormous yields of sugar with little depletion of soil fertility. The conversion of wood and agricultural waste products into sugar would require little additional agricultural land. The conversion of these sugars into proteins, fats, and vitamins through yeast production may be a practical method of increasing world food supplies, particularly in tropical areas.

It is improbable that yeast will ever provide a large proportion of our food requirements. Fed to livestock, yeast in excess of 5 or 10 per cent of the total food consumption has led to undesirable reactions. However, for human food it may be used at the rate of less than an ounce per day per person, as a supplementary ration. But even an ounce per day would provide some of the proteins, fats, and vitamins needed by hundreds of millions of people.

The most promising single new food source, initiated by H. A. Spoehr of the Carnegie Institution (106), is the mass culture of Chlorella, a single-celled algae. In the yields of normal crops, limiting factors include short growing seasons (in the temperate zone); utilization of only a small fraction of the available sunlight while the plants are young; excessive heat or cold; lack of an optimum supply of water and plant nutrients; the limited supply of carbon dioxide in the air; and the utilization of only parts of the plants for food. Algae grown in open ponds are little more efficient than most crop plants in converting solar energy into organic matter. But when grown in a closed system under optimum conditions, their efficiency can be increased tenfold to twentyfold, and all of their organic matter can be used for food. By growing algae in culture solutions in glass-covered trays or in transparent tubes, the optimum concentration of plant nutrients and carbon dioxide can be maintained. The usual mineral nutrients and trace elements can be controlled more accurately in a water solution than in the soil.

Carbon dioxide, which serves as the raw material for photosynthesis, constitutes only .03 per cent of atmospheric gasses. Most plants can use considerably higher concentrations of carbon dioxide. With increased carbon dioxide (up to about 0.1 per cent) there is a corresponding increase in the rate of photosynthesis in Chlorella. Culture chambers, since they are closed systems, permit efficient control of atmospheric conditions. The carbon-dioxide content is increased to 5 per cent to permit adequate diffusion from the air to the water in which the algae are grown (15). With optimum growing conditions (taking into consideration the carbon-dioxide content of the air, mineral nutrients, factors of temperature and light), it might be possible to produce over 17 tons of dried algae per acre of cultures per year, according to pilot-plant tests of Arthur D. Little, Inc. By using a strain of Chlorella better adapted to higher temperatures, and improving the general technique, higher yields might be realized. In any case these yields are far greater than those of ordinary field crops. A high yield of corn produces only about 3 tons of grain per acre; moreover corn contains only 10 or 12 per cent protein compared with about 50 per cent in dried Chlorella.

There are a number of obstacles in the culture of algae for food. A warm climate is necessary if the cultures are to be grown throughout the year without artificial heat; yet excessive sunlight is injurious to the growth of Chlorella.

There must be an abundant supply of water; but water is usually scarce in areas of abundant sunlight. Even though Chlorella has a much higher protein content, the cost would be excessive compared with that of corn, wheat, or soybeans.* Algae are nutritious; but for human food there are limits to its acceptibility both in terms of palatability and the proportion it can assume in the total diet. According to Fisher and Burlew (15), fresh undried material is generally palatable; but when the product is frozen and thawed there is a " gag factor " and an unpleasant aftertaste. The dried Chlorella alone is too strongly flavored to be used as a major part of the diet. Until Chlorella can be produced at much lower costs than present estimates indicate, and unless it can be made palatable enough to constitute a substantial part of the diet, it is not likely to prove a major food source.

The chemical synthesis of food and the production of edible algae are expensive processes requiring the services of highly trained operators. Modern agriculture in general requires specially trained skills in order to make effective use of the techniques, machines, fertilizers, fungicides, and equipment now necessary for efficient food production. Before these skills can be utilized in most of the world, many more people must be educated and trained.

The second great need of the modern world is an abundant source of energy. As we saw in Chapter 5, man and his domestic animals provide only a very small fraction of

---

* The cost of the trays or tubes is estimated at about $50,000 per acre, and the recovering and drying of the algae is an expensive process. The total cost of producing dried Chlorella is estimated at about 27 cents per pound (76).

the increasing amount of energy used in modern industry and transportation.* Nearly all of this energy has been obtained from capital reserves of coal and petroleum. If we are to think in terms of world industrialization, new sources of energy for heat and power must soon be developed.

Atomic power appears to be able to meet the demands for certain types of energy for a very long period of time. The pre-war estimates of available high-grade uranium ore would satisfy total energy needs for only a few years (102). In 1951 the President's Material Policy Commission concluded that by 1975 nuclear fuels might provide about one-fifth of our total energy needs. The recent development of the " breeder " reaction makes it possible to convert thorium into the fissionable uranium. These and other advances in the development of atomic energy have greatly expanded the potential sources of energy from atomic fission. It is now believed that atomic sources may produce about twenty times as much energy as the known deposits of coal and petroleum. But much depends upon the efficiency of the breeder reaction and the availability of sources of nuclear fuel. If the world's energy consumption is to continue to increase at recent rates the more optimistic estimates of nuclear energy resources would provide the needs of a growing world population for only a few hundred years.

Energy from atomic power is not expected to be prohibitive in cost. There are, however, some limitations in its

* The energy needs of the world have been increasing at an average rate of about 2 per cent annually since 1860; during the past 20 years energy consumption has increased at the rate of about 3 per cent per year, and the rate is accelerating (105).

use. It is not evident how atomic energy could be used in the production of pig iron, although electric furnaces, powered by atomic energy, could replace coal as a blast-furnace fuel, and hydrogen produced by electrolysis of water could replace coke as the chemical reducing agent in the blast furnace. At present it is also difficult to envisage the use of atomic energy as a source of power for automobiles, tractors, and airplanes. The atomic-power source must be shielded by heavy and bulky walls to avoid exposing the operator to dangerous amounts of ionizing radiation.

Perhaps it is unnecessary now to investigate new sources of renewable energy which might be available when the reserves of fissionable fuel become exhausted — but atomic power *is* based upon capital reserves. If the hydrogen bomb were harnessed for industrial power, our energy requirements would be solved indefinitely. Sir John Cockcroft, English physicist and Nobel Prizewinner, at the 1954 meeting of the British Association for the Advancement of Science expressed the opinion that the energy of nuclear fusion could be developed for peacetime use before the world reserves of uranium fuel are exhausted. Although hydrogen is now expensive to produce in the required form, there is an ample supply. According to Eugene Ayres (3), a cubic mile of sea water would provide enough hydrogen (if converted into helium at a 10-per-cent level of efficiency) to provide the world's energy needs, at the 1950 rate of consumption, for 30,000 years.

If the hydrogen bomb cannot be harnessed, capital reserves of energy must eventually be replaced by renewable resources. The fundamental source of all renewable energy is the sun. Solar energy is more than adequate to meet any probable future needs if it can be efficiently converted into mechanical, electrical, or chemical energy. Eugene Ayres (2) has estimated that the solar energy reaching the earth each day is more than 30,000 times as great as the energy now provided by coal, petroleum, and hydroelectric power.*

Nearly all of the solar radiation that reaches the earth is in turn reflected from the earth's surface, absorbed by the water and the air, used for the evaporation of water from the ocean or for the transpiration of plants. Very little is converted into chemical or potential electrical or mechanical energy. Although about 40 per cent of the total solar energy is used in evaporating ocean water, only a minute fraction (perhaps .002 per cent) could be recovered in the form of electrical or mechanical energy by utilizing all potential resources of water power. The transformation of solar energy into forms now available to man is shown in Figure 9.

The conversion of solar energy into potential chemical energy by photosynthesis uses perhaps 1.5 per cent of the total solar energy reaching the earth (86). Most of this energy is used by marine plants which, when converted

* In favorable locations the solar energy per acre of land surface each year may be equivalent to the energy of more than 1000 tons of coal; in the United States the solar energy per acre of land is equivalent to the energy contained in about 800 tons of coal. Our average per-capita energy consumption in 1950 was equivalent to about 8 tons of coal. Inasmuch as there are about 12 acres of land per person in this country, the solar energy per capita was equivalent to more than 9000 tons of coal — or about 1000 times our per-capita energy consumption in 1950. And our consumption of energy per capita is the highest in the world.

into fish, provide scarcely 3 per cent of man's food and practically no other source of energy. Land plants convert into available sources of chemical energy only about .05 per cent of the total solar energy reaching the earth. Including food from the sea and the electrical energy from hydroelectric plants, man now consumes less than .002 per cent of the total solar energy reaching the earth.

It seems quite possible that much more solar energy could be converted into chemical, electrical, and mechanical energy. Until recently, little research work has been done in this field; even now, research is limited to small-scale investigations carried on at relatively few centers.

One method of converting more solar energy into organic material is a more efficient utilization of natural photosynthesis by growing algae in a closed system (as mentioned on page 110 of this chapter). Algae could be used not only for food, but also for fuel. A ton of dried Chlorella contains nearly as much potential energy as a ton of coal. Depending on the efficiency achieved, 16 to 32 million acres devoted to algae factories could provide as much potential energy as was obtained in 1950 from fossil fuel, wood, and hydro-electric power.

But culture of algae for fuel appears uneconomical in the face of the present estimated cost of 27 cents per pound. The President's Material Policy Commission concluded that a new source of energy must not exceed 1.5 times present costs. In order to compete with present sources (and soon probably with atomic energy), the cost of dried algae would have to be reduced to 0.4 cents per pound — or one-sixtieth of present estimated costs (76).

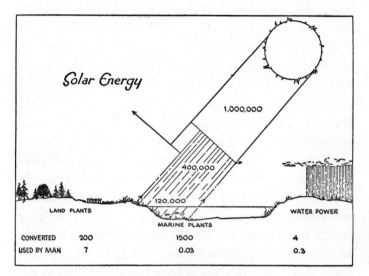

Solar Energy			
	1,000,000		
	400,000		
	120,000		
LAND PLANTS	MARINE PLANTS		WATER POWER
CONVERTED	200	1500	4
USED BY MAN	7	0.03	0.3

FIGURE 9

THE USES OF SOLAR ENERGY

Here the units of solar energy are given in trillions of kilowatt-hours electrical energy equivalent. Of the approximately 1,000,000 units reaching the earth's outer atmosphere each year, only about 400,000 units reach the land and seas, because of absorption and scattering of the energy as it passes through the atmosphere. About half of the radiation reaching the earth consists of wave lengths of no use in photosynthesis; much of this radiation is reflected and absorbed by barren or snow-covered land; and some is used for evaporation of water. As a result, only about 120,000 units are available for photosynthesis by plants. Only about 1.5 per cent of this energy is converted into organic material — approximately 200 units by land plants and 1500 units by marine algae.

Of the energy converted by land plants, man uses about 7 units each year (in the form of food, fiber, and wood); of the energy from marine sources, man uses about 0.03 units (largely in the form of fish). He also uses about 0.3 units from evaporation and rainfall (in the form of hydroelectric power).

Unless the nuclear reactions responsible for solar energy, recently developed in the H-bomb, can be used for peaceful purposes, the sun must continue to supply all of our energy needs in the future, as it has in the past.

(Data from *Energy Resources of the World,* and from Rabinowitz.)

Thus, the prospects of efficiently growing algae for fuel are not encouraging.

Direct use of the sun's energy for power has been experimented with for many years. By focusing sunlight on thin boiler tubes, it is possible to generate some power; but again the costs are high. In a favorable climate, it would take the light collectors spread over an area of one acre to produce 50 or 60 horsepower of continuous energy (52). Solar heaters of various types have been developed; but up to now they have been of practical value only in providing domestic hot water in areas with a mild climate and abundant sunshine. Space heating by trapping solar energy under glass and storing the heat for use at night or on cloudy days has been developed on an experimental scale (68). Several years ago the Bussey Institution was asked to test a solar heating plant in a small experimental greenhouse; the estimated cost of the heating plant was $25,000. Such a capital investment would bring the yearly cost of heating far beyond that of conventional methods. Perhaps economical methods of heat storage can be developed to make solar heating practical. Solar radiation as a direct source of power is available, but at present only under favorable climatic conditions and at prohibitive cost.

One of the most fascinating possibilities of utilizing solar energy involves the conversion of light to chemical energy by non-biological action. It seems probable that some chemical method could be developed which would convert solar energy into chemical energy as effectively as the chlorphyll does in plants. The major need is for some method of stabilizing the chemical energy produced, so that the products are not immediately combined. Promising results have been obtained by Lawrence J. Heidt and A. F. McMillan (48), although the proportion of energy conversion is low.

Thermoelectric conversion of solar energy is also possible; but at low temperatures the efficiency is only about 1 per cent. By concentrating the sunlight with lenses or mirrors, the efficiency may be increased to perhaps 3 or 4 per cent. Much more research along this line should certainly be carried on — the aim being efficient and practical conversion of solar into electrical energy (68).

The latest converter of solar energy is a solar battery developed by the Bell Telephone Laboratories. These batteries convert sunlight into electrical energy at a relatively high degree of efficiency — 50 watts of electrical energy per square yard of sunlit surface. According to Arthur D. Little's *Industrial Bulletin* (July 1954), a similar converter has been developed by the Wright Air Force Development Center; but in both cases " the cost of energy from such devices is much greater than from conventional fuels, largely because pure materials are needed."

Solar energy absorbed by land and water can also be utilized for heat and power. In many areas " heat pumps " provide an economical method for both heating and cooling houses. The heat pump converts the heat of earth, lake, or river into higher temperatures by compression of the circulating medium in winter and expansion of it for cooling in summer. Pipes carrying the heat from the ground are buried in the bottom of a pond or below the frost line in the earth. The major cost is that of the original installation, which, with the cost of electric power for pressure and circulation, amounts to a total expense not differing significantly from that of conventional heating systems. In areas where summer cooling is as important as winter heating, the cost may be less. Although there are practical limits in the use of heat pumps, they are likely to replace other methods in favorable areas, thereby considerably reducing the use of coal and oil (68).

To summarize this part of our survey, we can conclude that the world's expanding population needs more food. An industrial civilization must soon tap new sources of energy. Both agriculture and industry need machines which, in turn, consume vast quantities of our exhaustible capital resources of metals.

The new frontiers of science will undoubtedly make great advances in the production of both food and energy; but it takes decades to develop techniques and equipment and to attain commercial production. In the meantime world population is growing at a rate of more than 1 per cent per year — and the rate is accelerating.

For two-thirds of the world's people, birth rates are at or near the physiological maximum. These people do not have the motives, the knowledge, or the income necessary to use most of the modern contraceptive techniques. The world's greatest immediate need is a simple, effective, and inexpensive contraceptive which could be used at a low level of motivation. Preferably, it should be acceptable to those Western groups now opposed to the practice of " artificial " birth control.

Science seems to be on the verge of such a discovery. The pregnancy hormone prevents ovulation. This hormone is a steroid that can be synthesized and might not be excessive in cost. The use of such a hormone as an oral contraceptive would simply prevent ovulation, and without the release of the egg there could be no pregnancy. There should be no deleterious side effects, since the steroid occurs naturally during pregnancy.

It is possible that the more " primitive " peoples of the world have already discovered the oral contraceptive derivative from plants (just as they have discovered our food plants, the natural narcotics, and the stimulants used by " modern " man). According to Paul Henshaw, research director of the Planned Parenthood Federation, there are records in anthropological literature of dozens of plants that have been used as oral contraceptives (49). The use of bark or leaves of certain plants for contraceptive purposes has been developed independently by many peoples in different parts of the world. Although most of these reports must be included as part of local mythology, there is evidence that some of the plants used are effective. Lithospermum, used by Indian tribes of the southwestern United States, seems to be the most promising. The Indian women drank an infusion made from the roots of this plant to prevent pregnancy. B. P. Wiesner and John Judkin (126) in England have found that the daily consumption of a water extract of Lithospermum suppresses ovulation in women.

Lithospermum, a widely distributed genus of the Boraginaceae, is found in Europe, Asia, and the Americas (59). Some of the species (including *L. officinale* and *L. ruderale*, which are known to contain the contraceptive ingredients) are large perennial herbs. These could be grown as cultivated crops and harvested with ordinary haying machinery at low cost. The simplest and most immediately practicable method would be to package the dried leaves and stems and use them in the form of an herb tea.

The active ingredient of Lithospermum has not yet been isolated. Perhaps some of the other plant genera used for contraceptive purposes may provide a potent source that can be isolated in a concentrated form, eventually by chemical synthesis. Such a concentrated ingredient could be used in a contraceptive pill; it could be incorporated in a staple food such as sugar or salt, or in a basic cereal such as rice or wheat. The concentration could be regulated to effect the desired reduction in the birth rate, or untreated foods could be made available for women when they wanted another child.

An even more promising physiological contraceptive has been developed by Dr. S. N. Sanyal in India. He found that an oil obtained from the seeds of the common pea (*Pisum sativum*) greatly reduced pregnancy rates when injected into the muscles of women once each month. The oil was also found to be effective when taken orally in capsule form twice each month. Tests with 127 patients showed a reduction in the pregnancy rate of 73 per cent. According to Dr. Sanyal the effect of the drug is not injurious and is not an abortificant. Further work will be necessary; but the results published in the *International Medical Abstracts and Reviews* (1954) are promising.

The new frontiers of science should be able to make great contributions to both industry and agriculture. If the social sciences and religion could make equally significant progress in promoting rational thought, international cooperation, and the elimination of war, the world would indeed face a promising future. With the disappearance of primitive taboos regarding human reproduction and with an efficient means of controlling birth rates at all levels of society, it should be possible to prevent excessive population pressures in all parts of the world. If, however, population growth is not controlled effectively and rapidly, and if such large proportions of the world's income and resources continue to be squandered on war or the preparation for war, the new frontiers of science can do little to solve the problems of poverty, ignorance, and misfortune.

PART THREE

PROSPECTS FOR THE FUTURE

7
Two-thirds of the World

The modern Western nations, comprising about 15 per cent of the world's total population, have essentially completed their Demographic Transition (Chapter 3). Although they are depleting their reserves of capital resources at an alarming rate, they are in a position to develop the new frontiers of science; in a peaceful world present resources could be efficiently used to maintain high living standards for many decades. If the new frontiers of science are as successful in opening new sources of food and minerals as they have been in developing new sources of energy, the nations with controlled birth rates should be able to maintain high living standards indefinitely.

Can the rest of the world make a similar transition? The magnitude of the problem is suggested by the economic, cultural, and demographic data shown in Table 10.

The industrial development of the three demographic groups is reflected in the enormous differences in per-capita consumption of inanimate energy. Prospects for future industry are partially indicated by the amounts of coal and iron reserves. With the exception of China, the Group III countries lack coal; and China itself has meager reserves of iron ore.

Differences in economic status among the three groups are best shown by annual per-capita incomes. Before World War II, according to Point Four studies, the three

TABLE 10

ECONOMIC AND CULTURAL STATUS OF THE WORLD

	Demographic groups†		
	I	II	III
Population: millions (1950)	362	496	1550
Population: percentage of world total	15	21	64
Energy used per person per day (horsepower–hours)	27	6	1
Coal reserves: trillions of metric tons	3.3	1.7	0.5
Iron-ore reserves: billions of tons	65	104	24
Percentage of world's tractors (1951)	82	15	3
Motor vehicles per 1000 people	111	7	*
Annual income per person (1939 dollars)	461	154	41
Annual income per person (1950 dollars)	1000	300	77
Cultivated land per person: acres	1.5	1.7	0.7
Original calories per person per day	7500	4500	2500
Calories consumed per person per day	3040	2760	2150
Percentage of population in agriculture	20	50	70
Percentage of illiteracy	5	20	78
Life expectancy: years	63	52	30
Birth rates	16–24	25–30	40–45

† Demographic GROUP I includes North America, Western Europe, Australia, and New Zealand. GROUP II includes U.S.S.R, eastern and southern Europe, Japan, and Argentina. GROUP III includes Africa, Asia, the Middle East, and Latin America.
    * Less than 1.
    Data from Davis (28); Piquet (82); Spengler (105); U.N. *Demographic Yearbook,* 1952; U.N. *Statistical Papers,* Series H, No. 5 with revised estimates by E. E. Hagen (1954); U.S. Department of State (118); U.S. Department of State (119); Woytinsky (128).

demographic groups had per-capita incomes of $461, $154, and $41 respectively. The estimates for 1950 are approximately $1000, $300, and $77. Considering the depreciation of the dollar during the interim, the purchasing power per capita has increased in the Group I areas, has remained about the same in Group II countries, and has declined in the Group III countries.

Agricultural resources are shown by dietary levels and by the percentage of the working population engaged in agriculture. However, as we saw in Chapter 4, the actual calorie consumption is a poor index of dietary levels, because it does not reflect the quality of the diet. In the Group III countries, calories are derived largely from grains, roots, and tubers; in most of the Group I and some of the Group II countries, from 20 to 30 per cent of the food consumed is in the form of meat, milk, cheese, and poultry products. The conversion of food consumption in terms of original calories reflects both the quantity and quality of the food consumed. Pardoxical as it may seem, the greater the proportion of the population engaged in agriculture, the poorer are the diets of the people.

The differences in life expectancy reflect the living standards and the public-health facilities of the different areas. Death rates in some of the poorest countries, such as Ceylon, are very low because of special public-health programs; but these low rates cannot be maintained unless the production of food and other necessities of life are increased at least as fast as the population grows. Among the Group III nations, the high birth rate is the greatest obstacle to the successful achievement of high living standards.

In estimating future growth rates of the various demographic areas, we have drawn upon estimates of the Office of Intelligence Research of the State Department for the years 1950–55, and upon recent statistics from the *Population Index* (83). Predictions of population trends are nearly as hazardous as political forecasts. But, if past history is any guide, we can expect population growth in Group I countries to level off rapidly; in most of the Class II areas to continue at the rate of about 1.2 to 1.5 per cent per year for at least several decades; and in practically all of the Class III countries to increase rapidly and substantially.

The greatest obstacle to amelioration of conditions in underdeveloped areas is the apparently inevitable population growth during the Demographic Transition. If these countries cannot increase the means of subsistence rapidly, and if they must wait for the slow diffusion of cultural and moral values to establish motives for the control of the birth rate, there is little chance that many of these countries can *ever* achieve the Demographic Transition. If population growth absorbs all increased production, the inevitable result will be more people living in ignorance and poverty.

We shall now examine in more detail how these factors operate in typical countries of Group II and Group III.

In a rational world the transitional demographic areas of Group II should have no great difficulty in completing their development. With the exception of Japan, Greece, and Italy, the major nations of Group II are not overpopulated in relation to resources. They have adequate land to provide food for some population growth as well as sufficient resources for adequate industrial development.

The U.S.S.R. and her European satellites have hardly begun to adopt modern agricultural techniques. Industrialization could provide the necessary farm machinery and transportation if the Communists did not choose to use most of their industrial capacity, as well as much of their skilled manpower, for military purposes. Russia's subordination of science (particularly her agricultural science) to political ends is another major handicap (18). If Russian agriculture continues to follow Lysenko's outmoded scientific philosophy and technique, the food supply cannot possibly keep pace with population growth. Soviet opposition to birth control can retard progress toward the small-family pattern. By 1954, however, Russian birth rates had declined to 24 per thousand. Russia should have no difficulty in achieving the Demographic Transition by the end of this century.

With the possibility of new energy and mineral resources, Italy too might be able to achieve the Demographic Transition. Northern Italy, in fact, might well be included among the areas that have nearly completed the transition. The Italian birth rate is now lower than that of many of the Group I countries. Moderate emigration would help to relieve population pressure — provided that the birth rate continues to decline as rapidly as it has in recent years.

Argentina has ample rich and arable land. Even though the present political administration is not conducive to economic or educational progress, this country should have no difficulty in effecting a favorable balance between population and resources.

Among the Group II countries, Japan faces the greatest difficulty in completing the Demographic Transition. Yet Japan is often cited as an example of relatively rapid demographic progress. The only Oriental nation to have developed an industrial culture, Japan furnishes important clues as to how other Asiatic countries might progress, with borrowed industrial techniques and modern medical science. For this reason Japan will be given more attention than any other Group II country.

Before 1850 Japan probably had an essentially stationary population, with high birth rates and high death rates. It has been estimated that, when the country was opened to the West in 1870, the population was between 27 and 35 million. With a borrowed industrial culture, an able and industrious people, a colonial empire, and space for emigration, the population grew rapidly. Birth rates remained high while death rates decreased rapidly. By 1940 the population of the Japanese empire (including Formosa, Korea, Manchukuo, and other territories) had reached 105 million (112).

Even with a borrowed industrial culture, Japan could not make the Demographic Transition more rapidly or with less population growth than the average Western nation.* But in 1940 Japan seemed to have a good chance of completing the transition by the year 2000, with a population of 120 million in the homeland and more than 60 million in outlying areas and other countries.

However, Japan went to war and lost her colonial em-

---

* Since 1870 the population of Japan has already increased nearly 300 per cent; if Japan had kept her industrial empire, the population would almost certainly have increased 400 per cent before the completion of her Demographic Transition.

pire. She had been trying to follow England in the development of industry and an empire; but the time was too late for industrial monopoly, the frontiers of the world were becoming heavily populated, and her imperial plans were too ambitious.

Today Japan has a population of 84 million.* Without a colonial empire, and with most of her world markets closed, Japan is now in a desperate situation. Although she has a very efficient agriculture in terms of production per acre, the 0.2 acres per capita are not enough to provide a subsistence diet, even when supplemented by a productive fishing industry. The limits of the available land demand intensive cultivation of small farms, where low living standards are in turn conducive to high birth rates. Even with the restoration of foreign markets, the people of Japan can expect only subsistence living standards — unless the birth rate can be reduced rapidly to replacement levels.

The Group III countries, which have not yet started their Demographic Transition, are faced with difficult problems indeed. Asia and parts of Central America are densely populated. Africa and South America do not have the present resources needed for industry. In all these areas it will take much time, education, and financial investment to develop the needed energy from atomic-

---

* Since 1900 the population growth rate has been about 13 per one thousand (and even higher in the outlying territories). Today the birth rate is about 20. As a result of food imports and of American-sponsored public-health activities, death rates have been reduced to about 12 per one thousand.

power plants or hydroelectric installations. There are no remaining frontiers to absorb surplus populations and to provide imported food and raw materials.

Although modern medicine can substantially reduce death rates under even modest public-health programs, it has done practically nothing to aid in the control of birth rates. The examples of Puerto Rico, Mexico, and Ceylon have shown that the control of the death rate without control of the birth rate can result in population growth of nearly 3 per cent per year, even with low living standards and little more than subsistence diets.

The 1500 million people who have hardly started their Demographic Transition vary greatly in educational and economic status. In many of the poorest Group III countries, there are some people who enjoy high living standards and some who are well educated. But the great majority of the people in these countries are poor, illiterate, and hungry. Lacking the necessary skills, knowledge, and capital, these areas cannot efficiently begin to utilize the great advances in agriculture and industry which science has made available to modern man.

In a peaceful world of cooperation among nations, the people of Africa and South America should be able to achieve the Demographic Transition in the long run. With a population of 110 million, South America is not densely populated; about 80 per cent of the people live within 200 miles of the sea coast. Although the lack of coal precludes profitable heavy industry until atomic sources can be developed, the available reserves of hydroelectric power may be adequate for light industry, even though such power sources are generally remote from present population centers. Reserves of arable land should be adequate (although they are surely far less than have been estimated by some ecologists). However, the rain forests of the great Amazon basin are of doubtful value for potential agricultural development because of the rapid loss of organic matter and the leaching of the soil consequent upon forest clearing; nor are tropical rain forests of great value for lumber production. The diversity of species and the sparse distribution of valuable timber trees make logging operations expensive; South America, although it has as much forest land as North America, harvests only 5 per cent as much timber and actually imports lumber from the United States and Canada. In constructing a railroad in Brazil it was found cheaper to import ties from Australia than to cut suitable timber along the right of way. There are, however, possibilities for planted forests of timber, nut, and rubber trees, which would add to the economy of this area. Moreover, South America is rich in minerals, many of which are now exported to the United States.

In the long run, South America's greatest need appears to lie in the development of a modern agriculture. Great expanses of grasslands in the southern half of the continent are fertile and have adequate rainfall. An efficient agriculture, development of mineral resources, and new industrial resources may be able to meet the needs of a growing population. But an improved economy would soon be swamped by excessive population pressure unless the present growth rates of about 1.8 per cent annually are substantially reduced.

In many respects the demographic status of Africa is

less encouraging than that of South America. With a few minor exceptions Africa is not densely populated; it has a total population of 200 million. Because of higher death rates, population growth is little more than 1 per cent annually. But birth rates are very near the physiological maximum. Although Africa does not have coal in quantities adequate for heavy industry, it has greater potential hydroelectric power than any other continent. There are large reserves of some critical metals. Prospects for a highly productive agriculture are uncertain. There is ample land, but much of it is desert. The tropical forests can be used only at great expense in maintaining the organic matter of the soil and the necessary mineral elements when the forests are removed. The deciduous forest zone is on a laterite soil which is not high in fertility, but which might be profitably farmed with proper crop rotation and the use of mineral fertilizers. The grasslands are areas of generally low rainfall which could be used for some crops if the soil were handled carefully to avoid erosion from wind and rain. With proper land use and with the adoption of modern agriculture, it may be possible to increase food production very substantially; but whether it can be done economically in terms of labor costs is still open to question.

The countries of Central America present a more difficult problem. Several of them are densely populated in relation to agricultural resources. Rapid exploitation of capital oil and mineral reserves could at best provide only briefly for the needs of fast-growing populations. These Latin American countries have the highest growth rate of any of the major demographic areas; records indicate an excess of births over deaths of 30 per thousand — or 3 per cent per year. In Mexico the birth rates remain well over 40 per thousand while recent death rates are low (about 16 per thousand) — both in spite of diets deficient in calories and protective foods. Costa Rica in 1950 reported birth rates of 46.5 per thousand and death rates of 12.2; if these figures are accurate, they indicate a population increase of 3.4 per cent in a single year. Population pressure in Haiti and El Salvador is so acute that thousands die from malnutrition (121). Cuba and Costa Rica fare much better; they have agricultural resources which, if properly developed, could provide relatively high living standards, if excessive population growth were curtailed.

One of the greatest handicaps for much of Central America is the mountainous terrain with its lack of water. Attempts to meet the demands for food through primitive agricultural techniques have caused extensive soil erosion. Much of the land so abused should have remained in forests or grass (41).

Mexico, for example, cultivates nearly one acre per capita; yet the majority of her people live little above subsistence levels. The development of modern agricultural methods by the introduction and use of better varieties of crop plants, mineral fertilizers, crop rotation, insecticides, and fungicides should make it possible to increase yields very substantially. Modern agricultural techniques might well double yields per acre — possibly increase them as much as threefold or fourfold where there is adequate rainfall, or where fields can be irrigated.

Maximum increase in yields from land now cultivated might provide a modest 5000 original calories per day per person for the present population of 25 million.

In Mexico, more land could be brought into cultivation; William Vogt (121) estimates that 24 million additional acres could be cultivated. This new land might possibly provide for the present rate of population growth, at subsistence dietary levels, for another twenty-five years. If the population continues to grow after that, the food intake must decline until the death rate balances the birth rate. It is highly improbable that either industrialization or the exportation of oil and minerals could provide for substantial food imports. Yet Alberto León, professor of preventive medicine in the School of Medicine of Mexico's National University, has predicted an ultimate population of 125 million (65). It seems impossible that Mexico could achieve high living standards for a population of more than approximately 50 million; and even this figure is based upon possible rather than probable increased production. The birth rates must be reduced — and soon. Without a rapid improvement in its economy and a rapid decline in the birth rate, Mexico (like many other Latin American countries) cannot hope to make the Demographic Transition.

The Demographic Transition should be possible, then, in Africa and South America, and it might be possible in Central America with the aid of a few scientific miracles. On the other hand, the situation in eastern and southern Asia appears to be hopeless. In this area there are nearly 1200 million people (1950 figures), not including the Japanese. China has about 480 million people, India 360 million, Indonesia 77 million; and there are many millions more in the Philippine Islands, Burma, Ceylon, and the Near East. Birth rates in all these areas are high; population growth is limited by high death rates to about 1 per cent per year. Nearly all of these Asiatic countries are densely populated, and most of their arable land is already cultivated.

In China, farms average only several acres, and the total of cultivated land averages about half an acre per person. By intensive and skillful cultivation — and the conservation and use of all organic matter, including human manure — the farmers produce relatively high yields per acre. Because the farms are so small and because of the great amount of human labor used per acre, the production per farm worker is pathetically low — probably not more than 5 per cent of that of the average American farmer. The small size of the farms precludes the use of modern farm machinery, even if the Chinese farmer could afford to buy it. Even if farms were increased to twelve acres, they would still be too small to justify use of the kind of power machinery employed by American farmers. Moreover, it would be impossible effectively to increase farm size without simultaneously providing work for displaced farmers in industry. If farms were increased in size to twelve acres, only a third of the present number of farm laborers would be needed; but industry would not be able to absorb all the new workers.

China has little new land that could be brought into cultivation; but yields per acre could be increased considerably by the use of mineral fertilizers, modern insecticides, and modern fungicides. In western China, modern machinery might make it possible to cultivate the marginal lands at a profit, and some new land might be brought under irrigation. But, at best, increased yields from present crop land and production from new land would no more than double the food production for the present population. If China must look forward to at least a threefold increase in population during her Demographic Transition, much greater food supplies will be needed. With present agricultural techniques, there is no hope for such increase in production.

In regard to India, more specific information is available. It has been estimated that 75 per cent of the working population are engaged in the production and distribution of agricultural products. India cultivates nearly an acre per person; but because much of the land is poorer, and the farming less efficient, the Indian diet is inferior to that of the Chinese. India, too, would have to double yields per acre if her present crop land were to provide an adequate diet for the present population; such increased yields might be possible with modern agricultural techniques. But India's population is growing at the rate of more than 1 per cent per year.

In India, more land will have to be brought into cultivation. The present Indian five-year plan proposes to bring into cultivation 15 million more acres by 1956. Even if this is done, and if the new land proves twice as productive as land now cultivated, the increased food production would just about keep pace with population growth. During the five years the population could be expected to increase by at least 25 million people, if there were no serious famines or epidemics. Five such five-year plans would bring into cultivation all of the 75 million acres of arable land not now cultivated; during these twenty-five years the population, at present rates, would increase from 360 million to perhaps 450 million. But if death rates were reduced to 12 per thousand — as they have been in Ceylon — the population would be doubled in twenty-five years. It would be difficult if not impossible for Indian agriculture to keep pace with such growth for any significant period of time.

The prospects for increasing the standard of living through industrialization are just as discouraging. India has iron ore and other minerals essential for industry, but little coal of high quality. However, let us assume that with the aid of atomic energy an effective industry could be developed. William H. Forbes (38) has estimated that a capital investment of $3000 per worker might be adequate for establishing an Indian industrial plant (far less than the cost in the United States); he further assumes that one worker would support four other people. In order to get half of the present working population out of agriculture and into industry — the minimum ratio essential to provide even moderate living standards in a heavily populated area — about 25 million new industrial jobs must be made available. The capital investment would have to be about $75 billion — or about four times the present national income.

However, it would be very difficult for India to save more than 5 per cent of the national income for investment in industry; with a total national income of less than $20 billion, India would do well to raise $1 billion a year from internal sources. Even if we assume a rapid increase in agricultural production with a corresponding increase in national income, it would take more than twenty-five years to provide the needed industrial jobs for the present population.

But if the population continues to grow at even the present rate, agriculture and industry will have to support an additional 150 million people in twenty-five years; industry would then have to provide at least 15 million new jobs at a minimum total cost of about $50 billion. During a 25-year period, the initial cost of minimum industrialization plus the needs of a growing population would require well over $100 billion. India cannot possibly raise this amount of capital from savings. Other nations could help; but even if they provided all the capital needed for the initial stages it is very doubtful if India could raise the capital needed just to provide industrial jobs for the increased population resulting from present birth and death rates. With even a modest public-health program and increased food production, population growth might well reach 3 per cent annually. There is no possibility whatever that Indian industry and agriculture could meet the needs of such a rapidly growing population.

As we saw in Chapter 3, industrialization was an important factor in the Demographic Transition of Western Europe because it permitted imports of food in exchange for manufactured products. England today has to import half of her food to maintain adequate dietary levels; few countries now have large food surpluses and many of them have fast-growing populations themselves. Even with great advances in agriculture it would be very difficult to produce enough surplus food for even half of the present population of India; it would be altogether impossible to provide enough for a rapidly growing Indian population. (If all of the food produced in the United States were added to that now produced in India, it would provide only a Western European dietary level for India's present population.) The demand for industrial products will also decrease as the rest of the world becomes industrialized. India cannot hope to benefit from the same circumstances as the countries that enjoyed an industrial monopoly during the critical years of their transition. The large and increasing population of India precludes any relief of population pressure by industrialization as a means of increasing the food supply. At best, industrialization in India can contribute toward better transportation, communication, tools for agriculture, clothing, utilities, and housing. All such contributions are important in promoting the Demographic Transition; but little real progress can be expected until adequate food is assured.

We have also seen that emigration was an important factor in the release of population pressure for many of the countries of Western Europe. But this factor offers no relief for India. There are no new frontiers for population expansion; even if there were, emigration would not solve India's problem at the present stage of her demographic evolution. It would be impractical to think of moving 5 million Indians each year — and still more unthinkable that any country would accept even one year's surplus Indian population. (Unless these emigrants soon developed a small-family pattern, they would quickly overpopulate the country to which they migrated; with natural birthrates and controlled death rates, 5 million Indians could increase to nearly 100 million in a hundred years.) Nor would emigration release population pressure in India. With a little more food available for the remaining population, the death rates would decline and the population growth would continue at the same rate. If food supplies could be increased further, and death rates reduced to modern levels, India would have an annual population surplus not of 5 million but of 15 million.

Emigration cannot be an effective means of reducing pressures in a large and rapidly growing population. It offers no hope whatever in the case of India. The Dutch have attempted this solution in the case of Java by moving people to the outer islands, but without success. Only with a small population is there any hope that migration can solve the problem of excessive population pressure. Frank W. Notestein (74) states:

> In general . . . emigration will not check growth in the most important areas of population pressure at the present stage of their demographic evolution. It would be unfortunate to waste the open spaces of the world in a fashion that could only intensify future problems of adjustment. The empty regions of the world are none too plentiful and should be used to some lasting effect.

Rapid and drastic reduction of the birth rate appears to be the only rational and effective solution of India's population problem. But if control of the birth rate must depend upon the same slow development of motivation that accompanied urbanization in the Western world, if we must await the same slow cultural diffusion of the small-family pattern, the situation in India can only appear hopeless. As demographers and economists have frequently pointed out, a reduction in birth rates goes hand in hand with city life, industrial development, higher living standards, and education. In general, no country's birth rates have appreciably declined until annual average incomes per capita had reached the equivalent of about $200 (in terms of 1950 dollars) (105). If India follows the Western pattern of controlled fertility, the national income must be increased at least fourfold before any significant decline in the birth rate can be expected. Even the ambitious Bombay fifteen-year plan postulated only a twofold increase of income per capita, in order to reach $46 (in terms of 1939 dollars). India cannot wait for the slow cultural changes that have led to low birth rates in the Western nations.

The only possible solution for such countries as India appears to be a thorough educational program and the development of a contraceptive that requires little motivation for the control of family size. Experience in this country has shown that contraceptives now available, even if provided free of cost, will not be used by poor and uneducated people. It is probable, however, that in areas where poverty and ignorance are nearly universal, a large proportion of the people might prove intelligent enough to adopt improved contraceptive techniques if they were available.

The possibility of a rapid reduction in the birth rate of low-income rural populations has already been demonstrated in Japan. The program was started in 1948 by

Dr. Y. Koya, director of the national Institute of Public Health. Three rural villages were selected as typical of high-birth-rate areas. An educational program and the use of simple contraceptives reduced birth rates from about 40 in 1948 to less than 20 in 1952; and by 1954 the birth rate had declined to 13.6. Although the Japanese rural people are better educated and probably do not live quite so close to subsistence levels as the rural population in the rest of Asia, it is evident that an educational program *can* be effective in high-birth-rate areas.

Enormous problems confront eastern and southern Asia — an area containing half the world's population. Many of the paths of escape from excessive population pressure that permitted Western Europe to make the Demographic Transition are no longer open to the people of Asia. They must start their transition with populations large in relation to resources; with little new land that can be brought into cultivation; with no possibility of effective emigration; with limited industrial potentialities; and with no colonies to provide food in exchange for manufactured products.

If the control of the birth rate must depend upon the slow changes in cultural patterns, it is unlikely that a significant decline can be effected with a lower level of social and economic development than was needed in Western Europe. There can be little hope for the Demographic Transition in Asia and other overpopulated areas unless these nations utilize new contraceptive techniques and effective educational programs regarding contraception.

8

Escape from Poverty

In a rational world, and with aid from the new frontiers of science, it should be possible to provide adequate food, good health, and education for all of the world's people. Although many of the underdeveloped countries do not have the natural resources necessary to meet energy and mineral demands as great as ours, still it should be possible to provide adequate power and materials for the minimum essentials of industry and transportation. Throughout the world, there must be an efficient agriculture to provide adequate food and to release manpower for work in industry, transportation, education, and the arts and sciences. There must be facilities for general education and technical training, because the fruits of modern science cannot be digested by an illiterate people. There must be good transportation to carry food and raw materials to industrial centers and to move manufactured products from industrial centers to farms and villages. There must be good communication facilities for the coordination of industrial, government and educational activities. And there must be some leisure time for recreation and contemplation.

The problem of man's aims and responsibilities in a " One World " culture has barely begun to be explored by the Western nations. Relationships between the industrial nations and their undeveloped or underdeveloped neighbors — relationships established in the past — have made the problems in many respects more difficult to solve. But this experience should help us to avoid mistakes in the future.

Colonial imperialism promoted an increased production of food and raw material; it did much to control disease; it provided some modern transportation; and it maintained internal order in the underdeveloped areas. All of these measures fostered longer life and greater population growth. On the other hand, local industry was limited, there was little education, and local cultures and traditions were preserved. The native peoples were given little responsibility, and initiative was not encouraged. Neither the motives nor the means of reducing birth rates were developed. The increased production of the colonies was used to provide raw materials and higher living standards for the ruling industrial countries; but in the colonies themselves practically all of the remaining increase in production was used in supporting more people at subsistence levels. In many other underdeveloped areas of the world, the relatively independent countries fared little better.

Even without exploitation and with a minimum of racial prejudice, it is enormously difficult to spread the motives and means necessary for the Demographic Transition. Puerto Rico offers an example of the results to be expected if a rehabilitation program is based only upon financial aid and good intentions. In 1898 the population of Puerto Rico was about a million, birth rates were more

than 40 per one thousand, and the death rates were high.
There were no schools and no public-health service, and
the people lived in abject poverty. Almost from the beginning the United States contributed substantial sums to
improve Puerto Rico. During the past two decades
American relief funds have averaged nearly $50 million
per year, the approximate equivalent of Puerto Rico's
total insular budget (30). Schools have been built, colleges and experiment stations established, large imports
of food made possible by a subsidy economy, and a modest
public-health program developed. As a result the death
rate declined substantially. (In 1950 it was only 9.9 per
1000.) Meanwhile birth rates remained nearly as high
as they had been fifty years before. The inevitable consequence was rapid population growth — from 1 million
in 1898 to 2.2 million in 1950, plus nearly half a million
living in the continental United States. The present
growth rate of nearly 3 per cent per year, if continued,
will double the population in less than thirty years. Most
of the Puerto Ricans still live in poverty — and the net
effect of American aid has been to increase the difficulty
of working out a rational solution to their problems.

Various commissions of " experts " have investigated
Puerto Rico's problems during the past few decades, but
none has had the courage even to mention the obvious
need for lower birth rates. Puerto Rico's own legislature has recommended a birth-control program, but it has
been sabotaged in the name of religion. Robert Cook
(22) writes well to the point:

Too often, experts in the field of public administration, education, medicine, public health, and religion, are to all intents

and purposes biological illiterates. They can cause mass suffering in the name of the past, and sometimes in the name of religion. When such men expose millions of their fellow beings to the evils of starvation and disease they must be made aware of the ignorance and the immorality of their acts.

A modern civilization does bring many problems, many of which can be solved only with time and experience. Modern industry is depleting the world's resources at an alarming rate; modern medicine has resulted in explosive population growth; and the atomic scientists have released a power that could destroy our civilization. The complexities and frustrations of modern urban life have led many to abandon their civic responsibilities; and some have even accepted the authoritarian controls of Fascism and Communism. Many of these symptoms are, however, only the growing pains of a young civilization. Maturity should bring wisdom and moderation.

The peoples of the underdeveloped areas of the world would be wise to avoid the excessive waste, competition, and tempo of the Western world. Yet they must have adequate food, housing, clothing, and medical care. These needs have been stressed in the following terms in the Point Four program originated by President Truman:

These people in recent years have been stirred by a growing awareness of the possibilities of human advancement. They are seeking a fuller life and are striving to realize their full capacities. They aspire toward a higher standard of living and better health and physical well being. Under present circumstances their poverty is not merely a handicap to themselves. By leaving them unable to fulfill their reasonable aspirations, their misery makes them fertile ground for any ideology which will hold out to them promise, however false, of means towards a better life.

These dangers have long been realized. As Seneca observed in Roman times, " A hungry people will not endure reason, they will not listen to justice, and they will not bend to any prayers for mercy." And from the Chinese comes the old proverb, " It is difficult to tell the difference between right and wrong when the stomach is empty."

Perhaps the experiences of the depression years in the United States have helped to clarify the aims and the methods of the Point Four program. The State Department and its advisory committee do not envisage a world-wide system of relief. Their approach to the problems of economic progress is outlined in Point Four as follows:

National development must be based upon national resources and must come largely from the people concerned. Assistance and encouragement from abroad can help, but real achievement must depend fundamentally upon the will and determination of the people and the government involved. In the last analysis, economic progress depends not only upon the resources, but upon the resourcefulness of the people. It is closely related to their habits and attitudes of work, saving, venturesomeness, and adaptability. It depends also upon the sound functioning of their governments.

Even though mistakes have been made in the past, there are projects in the underdeveloped countries of the world that might well serve as patterns for Point Four and similar programs. In 1944, for instance, the United Fruit Company established an agricultural school near Tegucigalpa, Honduras, for the education of boys from all Spanish-speaking Latin-American countries. The school provides food, housing, clothes, and medical care for 160 boys. The boys are trained for three years in

both basic and practical agriculture. None of the gradu-
ates is permitted to work for the United Fruit Company;
they are encouraged to join experiment stations, become
agricultural extension agents, or develop their own farms
in their respective countries. Latin-Americans consider
the school as a truly Pan-American institution, even
though it is financed by an American business firm.

For many years the Rockefeller Foundation was active
in supporting public-health activities in Latin America.
This program was very successful in reducing death
rates, because relatively simple medical techniques of
sanitation, vaccination, and sewage disposal could almost
eliminate some of the major diseases and epidemics. For
instance, as we saw in Chapter 7, Mexico became one of
the fastest-growing countries in the world. But dietary
standards remained low; the average Mexican consumed
only 2000 calories per day, and this largely from corn and
beans. As the population grew, even less food was available per capita.

The Rockefeller Foundation realized that there was
little virtue in controlling epidemics only to allow more
prolonged deaths from malnutrition or starvation. In
1943, therefore, the Foundation, in cooperation with the
Mexican government, established a project to increase
agricultural production. A survey was made by Dr.
George Harrar, assisted by a team of consultants.* They
found that yields of corn, wheat, and beans were very low,
partly because of poor varieties and partly because of un-
productive and primitive farm practices. Dr. Harrar

* Richard Bradfield of Cornell, Paul Mangelsdorf of Harvard, and
E. C. Stakman of the University of Minnesota.

began to improve the corn, the basic food supply of Mexico. Varieties of corn were collected and tested at the Mexican National College of Agriculture at Chipingo. By 1949 Harrar and his associates had developed eight good hybrid strains and enough seed to plant a million acres. By 1950, for the first time in several decades, Mexico did not have to import corn, and by 1952 crop yields had been doubled in large areas.

The agricultural program has been very successful and food production has been increased about 50 per cent during the past decade. But the population has increased nearly 30 per cent in the same period, and is growing at a rate that would double the population in less than thirty years. It should be easy enough to double Mexico's agricultural production in less than thirty years; but this increase would be necessary just to provide a really adequate diet for the present population of 27 million. Agricultural production cannot increase indefinitely.

The Rockefeller Foundation realized the complexities of the problem. Several years ago, therefore, it organized an agency to study, among other things, ways and means of inducing the Mexicans to reduce their birth rates. This project was aborted before it was born. But at least the basic problem had been recognized by the Foundation.

At the technical level we have in the United States the world's best organization for maintaining liaison between the science and practice of agriculture — the Extension Service of the U.S. Department of Agriculture. Although it is relatively young, it is perhaps the best exponent of adult education in the world today. The activities of the Extension Service are based upon the assumption that the individual farmer can seldom keep pace with new scientific and technical development in agriculture. It is the function of the county agent to interest agricultural communities in new methods and in the adoption of farm practices that aid soil conservation and increase production. Although the experiment station, the agricultural colleges, and exceptional farmers determine the best farm practices and develop the best crop varieties for a given area, it is the county agent who demonstrates the value of these scientific contributions at the production level.

An understanding of world agricultural problems at the top level is necessary; but it is impotent unless new techniques and new crops are actively utilized by individual farmers. An extension service composed largely of native personnel is needed to bring the relevant techniques of agriculture to farmers of the underdeveloped areas. But it takes time to educate and train the needed personnel, and time is a critical factor.

No program of Western aid to the underdeveloped countries can succeed unless the men selected to carry on the work have something of the missionary spirit — a sincere desire to serve, some acquaintance with local mores, and a knowledge of the language. The Christian missionaries have been successful in creating good will and cooperation because of their independence of government agencies. They promulgate no political propaganda, they learn the language and the customs of the community, and they sponsor educational programs.

There are also many reasons why development programs should ultimately be sponsored and coordinated by an international organization such as the United Nations.

Such a group would not be suspected of playing power politics, and its objectives would be less subject to the bias of national interest. Because of wide experience in the tropics, Dutch and English experts might be particularly suited to serve as agricultural advisers in tropical areas. It is probable that Latin-American technicians would have a better understanding than experts from North America or Western Europe of the social problems in such an area as Africa.

Help from the Western world must include more than technical aid in agriculture and industry. At a recent symposium on world agriculture, sponsored by the American Association for the Advancement of Science, the imposing panel of experts agreed that food production could be increased very substantially in most of the underdeveloped areas of the world. The major obstacle in many areas would be neither the soil nor the climate, but the difficulty of inducing local farmers to cooperate and to abandon primitive practices. When asked if any efforts had been made to study these social factors, the experts had to admit that nothing had been done in the field of the social sciences.

Any program for the agricultural and industrial development of the world will require capital investments which most of the underdeveloped countries cannot supply. The cost of an adequate United Nations or Point Four program would be high, and the Western nations would inevitably bear most of the cost. It has been estimated by Raushenbush (Table 11) that an adequate program would cost nearly $500 billion over a fifty-year period. Such expenditures would be far from adequate if past mistakes were repeated; but if the funds were properly expended they would go far toward establishing satisfactory educational and economic conditions.

The world could afford to spend far more than the proposed fifty-year budget if war could be prevented. Stringfellow Barr (6) has estimated that World War II

TABLE 11

RAUSHENBUSH'S PROJECTION OF TRENDS FOR ASIA, AFRICA, AND LATIN AMERICA

	Population (millions)	Growth rate	Farm labor (percent)	New land (millions of acres)	Per-capita income (dollars)	Cumulative cost (billions of dollars)
1951 A.D.	1644	1.18%	75	3	103	9
1960	1821	1.12%	71	265	121	65
1970	2036	1.07%	66	532	146	143
1980	2256	1.01%	61	785	177	232
1990	2485	0.94%	56	777	215	334
2000 A.D.	2721	0.89%	49	758	261	449

Data from Raushenbush (88).

cost the United States alone more than $300 billion, and that the cost to the world (in money spent and property destroyed) was about $2000 billion. The present "cold" war could cost the world more than $2000 billion if long continued, and a "hot" war could wreck modern civilization.

The prospects for speedily eliminating war or the preparation for war are not happy. The first steps toward such a goal might well include a careful program for world rehabilitation. If all major nations allotted only 10 per cent of their military budgets to the United Nations for a Point Four program, the contribution would greatly enhance the prospects for world peace by beginning to eliminate poverty and hunger. Such a " tithe for peace " not only would reduce military expenditures, but would encourage nations to reduce their military budgets. Eventually military expenditures might be reduced to such a level that even larger sums could be made available for world rehabilitation. If any major nation refused to take part in such a program, the underdeveloped countries might well question its professions of dedication to peace and the brotherhood of man.

We are often told that man's progress is more dependent upon spiritual values than upon material development. In many respects this is true; but the implication that spiritual values are incompatible with the advances of science is contrary to the facts. The role of science in spiritual development has been well summarized by the Chinese statesman and philosopher Hu Shih:

It took over a thousand years for a portion of mankind to emerge from the civilization based upon the religion of defeatism which glorified poverty and sanctified disease, and slowly build up a civilization which glorifies life and combats poverty. The change has come by development of science and machinery.

That civilization which makes the fullest possible use of human ingenuity and intelligence in search of truth in order to control nature and transfer matter for the service of mankind, to liberate the human spirit from ignorance, superstition and slavery to the forces of nature and to reform social and political institutions for the benefit of the greatest number — such a civilization is highly idealistic and spiritual.

9

The Obstacles of Tradition

Even with a rational program and missionary zeal, the work of combatting poverty and ignorance in much of the world will be a difficult one. To ignore the problems will only be to invite greater ones. Although the economists associated with such organizations as the United Nations and the Public Affairs Institute (sponsored by the Foundation for World Government) are well aware of the problems of a rapidly growing population during the Demographic Transition of underdeveloped countries, they are not realistic in dealing with those problems. It is well known that as per-capita income rises the birth rate declines, and that increased income is generally correlated with industrialization and urbanization. Thus it is easy to draw the conclusion that we need only develop industry to induce more people to leave farms and move to industrial centers.

Seymour Harris (45) proposes an extensive industrial program for the underdeveloped countries of Asia, Africa, and Latin America without a realistic appraisal of industrial resources. Nor does he indicate how industrialization could supply the enormous quantities of food needed in Asia. Perhaps the greatest lack of realism in Harris' estimates is his failure to provide for the excess rural pop-

ulation. He assumes, for example, that in Asia the farm
population could be reduced from 73 per cent (in 1950)
to 53 per cent (in 2000); but in fact, because of population growth, the absolute numbers of workers in agriculture would *increase*. The Asian farmer is already oper-
ating under the pressure of diminishing returns per capita
because of inadequate land.*   To reduce his holdings,
even with more intensive cultivation, would further de-
press his already precarious living standards.

Similar population and economic projections have been
made by Raushenbush (88), as shown in Table 11.   He
assumes that population growth rates will never exceed
1.18 per cent per year at any time during the next fifty
years, and that at the end of that time the growth rate
will be only 0.9 per cent annually.   Such a growth rate
would not be excessive if death rates were low and the
rate of industrial and agricultural production equaled or
exceeded the rate of population growth.   But many of
these areas are already densely populated and are not
rich in natural resources.

Moreover, these estimates for population growth are
themselves far from realistic.   In order to project growth
rates as low as 1.0 or 1.18 per cent annually, it is necessary to assume either that death rates will remain at high
levels or that birth rates can be reduced to half the present levels within a few years.   If adequate food is available, a relatively modest public-health program can reduce
death rates to 15 per thousand.   But birth rates, almost
certainly, would remain above 40 per thousand for at

---

* The average is 3.5 acres per farm in China; 5 acres in India; and 3
acres in Java.

least several decades — resulting in an annual growth rate of 2.5 per cent or more. During recent years growth rates of nearly 3 per cent annually have occurred in Puerto Rico, Mexico, and Ceylon, and for all of Central and South America the average annual growth rate for the decade 1936–45 was more than 2 per cent (114). Yet Raushenbush assumes that at no time during the next fifty years in Asia, Africa, and Latin America will the growth rate of the population exceed 1.18 per cent!

It is true that, with an increase in income, urbanization, and education, birth rates decline. But Raushenbush's projection of correlations based upon recent trends in the Western nations are hardly applicable to areas where the Demographic Transition has only started. The experience of Japan (discussed in Chapter 7) would seem to provide a much more rational and realistic basis for predicting demographic trends in Asia. In a study of the dynamics of population in Japan, Irene Treuber and Edwin Beal (112) have discussed the basic population problem of Asia:

The dynamics of fertility decline in Japan during the three-quarters of a century since the opening to the West, offer little basis for optimism with reference to the possibilities of an early cessation of population growth in the overcrowded regions of Asia. . . . If the same situation is to occur in the great overcrowded regions of Asiatic mainland, the race between the expansion of economic opportunity and the accelerated population growth produced by mortality control would seem to be hopeless. The major demographic need of Asia thus becomes that of devising ways by which the rate of increase of the peasants can be controlled much more rapidly than it would be if reliance were placed solely on the slow processes of cultural diffusion from the cities to the countryside.

Nevertheless, Seymour Harris states that " Japan's experience so far has also been promising " (45).

The reluctance to face the major demographic problem takes many forms. There are, for instance, some who contend that the declining birth rates of modern Western nations represent either a biological trend or phenomena automatically accompanying the progress of civilization. It is therefore necessary to show that there is no evidence of any significant decline in the natural fecundity of the human species.

Various proposals of great ingenuity have been offered to explain the decline of birth rates in the West. They have in common the refusal to recognize this as a mature application of Malthusian " preventive checks " in achieving the Demographic Transition. Kirtley Mather claims (70):

Indeed there is some evidence, though inconclusive as yet, that declining birth rates are due as much to physical factors of the human body as to mental attitudes toward the bearing and rearing of children. The approach towards a stationary population seems to be a perfectly normal accompaniment of the transition from the youthful to the mature stage in the evolution of man, an approach that is now being made more rapidly by the white race than by any other segment of the human family.

The editor of *Commonweal* (September 5, 1941), in deploring the low birth rates of Catholics in the United States, suggested that " birth control may not be a determining factor in population trends." He concluded that " there is much evidence that the . . . assumption has its own validity " — although he presented no such evidence.

The fact that family size decreases with education has led some people to conclude that " education sterilizes." Mrs. Breckinridge, a social worker among the " fruitful mountaineers " of Kentucky, maintains that " with few exceptions the urban educated citizen is incapable of producing a large family " (55). On the other hand, Sheldon and Hartl (100) claim that the poor and ignorant mothers of Boston's delinquent youths in the Hayden Goodwill Institute are relatively infertile, even though they are almost constantly exposed to the possibility of pregnancy. These authors suggest that, if two hundred Vassar girls selected at random were to spend twenty years in a sociological experiment in which the object was to get pregnant as frequently as possible, they would far outstrip the mothers of the delinquent boys in the number of offspring produced.

Josue de Castro, chairman of the executive council of the Food and Agriculture Organization of the United Nations, has revived an old theory to explain the low birth rates of the people of the modern Western nations and the high birth rates of the Indians and Chinese. In his recent book *The Geography of Hunger,* he maintains that a diet high in proteins, especially the proteins from animal sources (meat, milk, and eggs), results in decreased fertility, while a meager carbohydrate diet promotes high fertility. De Castro states: " Hunger is responsible for the overproduction of human beings, excessive in number and inferior in quality, who are hurled blindly into the demographic metabolism of the world " (16).

In view of the apparent acceptance of De Castro's

theory by eminent people in various countries, and the
apparent approval of his book by Sir John Boyd-Orr,
former chairman of the Food and Agriculture Organization of the United Nations, his theory should be examined
in some detail. De Castro compares J. R. Slonaker's conclusions from experiments with rats with the relationship
between human diet and birth rates in selected countries
of the world. Slonaker (103) fed rats with food varying
in protein content from 10 to 26 per cent. (The protein
from animal sources varied from about 5 to 23 per cent.)
His experiment showed that a total protein content of 14
per cent gave the highest degree of fertility. With higher
protein consumption, there was less fertility; rats on a 25-
per-cent protein diet produced only one-fourth as many
offspring as those on a 14-per-cent protein diet. A high-
protein diet reduced not only fertility, but also viability,
growth rate, activity, time of maturity, and longevity.
Obviously, this particular high-protein diet was deleterious in every respect.

However, in an earlier experiment (not mentioned by
De Castro), Slonaker and Card (104) had found that rats
fed on a diet restricted to corn and vegetables were so
sterile that by the third generation the family became extinct. (When 2 or 3 grams of meat scraps were added to
the corn and vegetable diet, fecundity was more than
doubled.) Sherman and Campbell (101) found that one
part of dried milk added to five parts of wheat provided a
better diet than wheat alone.* More recently, Davis (27)

* When the milk was increased to two parts dried milk, the diet was
further improved. Rats receiving two parts milk in the diet grew larger,
matured earlier, had a much longer reproductive span, lived longer, and
were three times as fertile as the rats receiving only one part milk plus
five parts wheat in their diet.

found that well-fed city rats were not only larger than their poorly fed country cousins but more than twice as fertile.

All of these experiments show that the well-fed rats and ones that consumed a moderate amount of animal protein grew larger, matured earlier, lived longer, were more active, and proved more fertile than rats that ate only plant products. It is true that Slonaker's high-protein diet reduced fertility; but it also reduced size, longevity, and activity — factors not found in well-fed populations such as ours. Excessive overweight does reduce fertility in livestock and presumably in man; but this is not an important factor among the great majority of couples during the most fertile years.

De Castro presents a list of countries to show that people who live largely on a carbohydrate diet have high birth rates, and that those who get much of their food from animal sources have low birth rates. In general, birth rates are high in the countries with poor diets and low in the countries with good diets.*

It can be shown that, in the demographic Group I countries of the world, the average animal protein consumption per person per day is 1.6 ounces; in Group II countries, 0.9; and in Group III countries, 0.3. The birth rates for the three demographic areas are about 20, 30, and 40 respectively. However, there is no evidence that there is any causal relationship between protein intake and fertility. There is also a high negative correlation between birth rates and the number of motor vehi-

* Among the countries listed, Formosa had the poorest diet (with an average consumption of only 4.7 grams of animal protein per day per person) and a birth rate of 45.6; Sweden, with an average consumption of 62.6 grams of animal protein, had a birth rate of only 15.0.

cles, literacy, and telephones per thousand of population
(105). It would be just as logical to assume that people
who spend much of their time riding, talking, or reading
have low birth rates because they have so little time for
reproduction.

TABLE 12

THE RELATION BETWEEN ANIMAL–PROTEIN CONSUMPTION
AND BIRTH RATES

	Protein consumption (grams per day per person)	1950 birth rates
Venezuela	23	43.0
Mexico	16	43.7
Ceylon	6	40.2
New Zealand	65	25.9
Greece	18	26.1
Japan	8	25.6
Ireland	50	21.0
France	40	20.4
Italy	20	19.6
Sweden	58	16.4
Belgium	36	16.5
Austria	27	15.6

Data from United Nations, *World Social Situation* (1952); and from
Population Index, July 1952. The Japanese birth rate is given for 1951.

We find no significant causal relationship between animal protein consumption and human birth rates. Countries that vary greatly in per-capita consumption of animal proteins often have very similar birth rates (Table
12). The people of Venezuela consume nearly four times
as much protein as the people of Ceylon; yet birth rates
are high in both countries. The Venezuelans consume
little more meat than the Italians; but their birth rate is

more than twice as high. The New Zealanders consume eight times as much meat as the Japanese; yet their birth rates are similar.*

In the United States meat consumption happens to show, statistically, a positive correlation with birth rates. During the period from 1900 to 1950, meat consumption reached its peak in 1908, with a per-capita consumption of 163 pounds (116); the birth rate in 1909 was 27. The consumption of meat in 1935 reached its lowest level with a per-capita consumption of 116 pounds; in the following year the birth rate was 17 per thousand. With the return of more prosperous times, the per-capita meat consumption reached 153 pounds in 1946, and the birth rate increased to nearly 26 per thousand in 1947.

This does not, however, indicate a causal relationship between meat consumption and fertility. In 1908 the practice of contraception was not as prevalent as it became in later years. In the depression year of 1935, people could not afford to eat as much meat or to have as many children. In 1946 — with the return of the servicemen, more prosperous times, and high marriage rates — both meat consumption and pregnancy increased substantially.

There is no evidence to support De Castro's conclusion that high birth rates in man are caused by diets deficient in animal proteins. We can only hope that as chairman of the executive council of the Food and Agriculture

* The Eskimos consume more protein than any other ethnic group, 45 per cent of their food being in the form of animal proteins; yet their birth rate of 47 is among the highest in the world, according to a U.S. Census survey of selected villages (53). Hrdlička, in a survey of twelve Eskimo villages, found that 68.8 per cent of the women either were pregnant or had borne a child during the year.

Organization he will base his recommendations upon more substantial grounds than he has used in attempting to solve the world's population problem.

Warren Thompson (111) contends that there may be some increase in sterility among the inhabitants of our cities because of the stress of modern life. But it would not be enough to account for more than a small fraction of the decline in birth rates.

There is, in fact, no evidence that the low birth rates of Western nations are due either to evolutionary trends, to education *per se,* or to ample food. If modern civilization, education, and ample diets were responsible for low birth rates, it would seem strange that Americans spend at least $250,000,000 per year for contraceptives (39).

Raymond Pearl (77) found a high negative correlation between the practice of contraception and family size in the United States. John Rock (91), in a discussion of the cause of low birth rates in the United States, concludes:

Nor is it because coitus is not performed. There are few happily married Americans between twenty and forty years of age who do not have intercourse at least once a week. Some other suppressive measures are in force. Gynecologists well know that most American couples use one or another form of contraception. . . . My experience with both clinic and private patients is that the incidence, for variable periods, of contraception, not including complete abstinence, is of the order of 90 per cent.*

Let us assume that living standards throughout the world can be raised to reasonable levels, that the United

* Dr. Rock practices medicine in Boston, where birth control is said to be " against God's law."

Nations can maintain world peace, and that population growth can be controlled by preventive checks so that population pressure will not bear too heavily on the means of subsistence. Could such a civilization long survive? Sir Charles Galton Darwin (26) thinks that there would be little hope. In his book *The Next Million Years* he envisages the depletion of the world's fossil fuels within a few hundred years, with no adequate substitutes to power a modern industrial civilization. He has grave doubts about the possibility of reducing birth rates in most of the world. Even if an essentially stationary population were attained, the " master race " complex might lead one country or group of people to increase birth rates in an attempt to expand and possess the earth. Differential birth rates would destroy the " creative minority." The present " Golden Age " of man would soon pass, as earlier civilizations have passed, to be followed by a struggle for mere subsistence in all parts of the world.

There is some basis for Darwin's assumption that a prosperous, stationary population might degenerate and could not survive in a strongly competitive world. In all countries where population growth has been controlled by preventive checks, there has been a high correlation between socio-economic status and birth rates. The parents with the lowest incomes and least education have the largest families, while the more prosperous and educated people have the lowest birth rates. A survey based upon the 1940 census of the United States showed that women who had graduated from college had an average of only 1.2 children, compared with 4.3 children for women who had only one to four years of education in primary schools (22). A comparable differential birth rate is found among economic groups; during the depression year of 1935 the only urban families who had birth rates above replacement levels were those on relief. Family size is correlated with intelligence, as measured by intelligence tests; the larger the family the lower the intelligence of both parents and children (22).

Whether poverty and ignorance are due to heredity or to environment, the immediate result in either case is a decline in the ability and performance of the general population. Studies made in both England and the United States have shown a decline in the average intelligence quotient of about 1 to 2 per cent per generation (22); but the data are not entirely adequate and the causal factors, if any, can hardly be evaluated at present. Certainly, in a society with equal opportunities for all, the higher birth rates of the lowest socio-economic classes would be dysgenic and could lead to a decline in the average intelligence of the population.

The rise and fall of past civilizations has been attributed to many causes, including differential birth rates and the decline of intelligence. In an analysis of Toynbee's *A Study of History*, S. C. Reed (90) points out that an average civilization of the past has lasted about eight hundred years, or the equivalent of thirty-one generations. He concludes that even a small decline in the mental ability during thirty generations might well result in the collapse of a civilization. Sir Charles Galton Darwin also believes that the loss of the " creative minority " has been an important factor in the decline of past civilizations.

Even if we assume that differential birth rates in Western nations have been dysgenic, there is evidence that they are only a transitional state during the Demographic Transition. We might expect that, with general education and better living conditions for all, differential birth rates would diminish, as they have in Sweden. William Vogt has recently shown that the lower socio-economic groups in Sweden do not have larger families than the more educated and prosperous members of the population. There is evidence of similar trends in some of the other Western nations.

A *laissez-faire* policy toward population control is at least implied in the proposals of such international agencies as the United Nations, the Point Four organization, and the Public Affairs Institute. As people become educated and develop economic and moral responsibilities, they control their birth rates with or without modern contraceptives and in spite of primitive religious taboos or legal restrictions. This, it is argued, was the course followed by the people of Western Europe; the rest of the world must follow the same pattern.

But it took more than a century for the western countries to attain a favorable balance between births and deaths, with the consequent increase in living standards. The densely populated areas of Asia, for example, cannot wait for such a slow transition, with its inevitable increase in population growth. Already overpopulated, they do not have the potential resources, the land, or the new frontiers to provide adequate living standards for many more people.

The need for a rapid transition is recognized by economists: yet they propose only the indirect and tragically slow effects of industrialization, urbanization, and higher living standards as the means of motivation in reducing birth rates.

A reluctance to disturb primitive social customs and superstitions conducive to high birth rates, combined with a determination to disturb old social balances induced by high death rates, was one of the great mistakes of colonialism. Yet many economists are not realistic in dealing with the problems of social balances. The problem has been presented by Raushenbush as follows (88):

> The desire of young men and women to live their lives with the future and the past through children is a very intimate matter. In many parts of the world, it is tied up with profound religious beliefs, and connected to concepts of personal duties to ancestors and God. There are age-old family and community mores that would have to be disrupted. These are difficult matters for any government to deal with which accepts the belief in the free right of people to determine the most important decisions of their lives.

Raushenbush does not seem to realize that these people simply do not have the means or the knowledge " to determine the most important decision of their lives." They are slaves of their natural instincts — instincts that were essential in primitive man if the human race was to survive, but that are now dangerous for civilization. Although cultural and religious mores, and the actual performance of the human race during the past three hundred years, would seem to indicate approval of large families, it is improbable that the average woman wants many children. Public-opinion surveys made in the United States

(62), Puerto Rico (46), and India (29) show that in all of these diverse communities the response was essentially the same: practically all women want more than one child, but few want more than four and the majority want only two or three.

The belief that poor and uneducated people will not adopt any form of contraception is based largely upon the differential birth rates in the Western nations. It is true that in these countries high birth rates are associated with ignorance and poverty. But it is also in these countries that we find the greatest opposition to birth control from religious and government agencies. As Bertrand Russell (95) has observed, birth control is subject to less superstition in Asia than it is in Massachusetts and Connecticut. Nehru is the only eminent political leader who has had the courage to recognize the necessity for controlling birth rates, and to include birth control in a national public health program.

The existence of poverty and illiteracy in the undeveloped countries of the world does not mean that the people of these countries lack innate intelligence and are incapable of rational thought. Faced with the prospect of having seven or eight children in order to insure the survival of two or three, or limiting family size so that the two or three children born have reasonable living standards and a good chance for survival, most parents would have little difficulty in making a choice. Large families among the poor and uneducated are not the result of choice, but of ignorance or irresponsibility. The effective practice of contraception requires a fairly high level of motivation and foresight. But the possibility of introducing physiological or other simple contraceptives offers a much more optimistic outlook. Modern medicine is so effective in controlling death rates that birth rates must be reduced very rapidly if excessive population growth is to be prevented. If, while death rates are reduced to Western levels in a few years, the reduction of the birth rate is delayed for even a few decades, any probable increase in agricultural and industrial production would be swamped by population pressure.

The major demographic needs of Asia and other critical areas cannot be met by controlling birth rates after the indirect fashion established in our Western patterns. A simple, inexpensive, and acceptable contraceptive technique must be developed. If necessary, an effective physiological contraceptive could be added to some basic food such as salt or sugar, so that pregnancy would be possible only by deliberately avoiding the treated food. It is almost certain that such oral contraceptives could be developed in a few years. Unfortunately, however, it is equally certain that no government agency or public institution in the United States would sponsor such a project, for fear of political or economic reprisal. Nor would the United Nations be likely to approve such a program because of Catholic and Communist opposition (to be discussed in Chapter 10).

The survival of primitive taboos and ancient creeds in this field reflects only a part of the distrust of intelligence that threatens the modern world. Our modern civilization has been made possible by great advances in science. Without expanding the frontiers of science, an industrial civilization cannot long survive. Scientific research and

technical skills require intelligence and training. Knowledge and education in other fields are equally important.
As Bertrand Russell puts it (95):

Wisdom in international affairs requires a knowledge of
geography [*but Harvard recently abolished its department of
geography*], an acquaintance with the habits of various nations
[*but only our missionaries seem to have any real knowledge of
the people of Asia*], and a capacity for seeing how the world
looks from a point of view that is not your own [*but witness
our difficulties in diplomatic negotiations*], none of which can
be obtained without intelligence. Our great democracies still
tend to think that a stupid man is more likely to be honest
than a clever man, and our politicians take advantage of this
prejudice by pretending to be even more stupid than nature
made them.

This hatred of intelligence and rational thought was
reflected in the efforts to make science subservient to political philosophy in both Hitler's Germany and the Soviet
Union (18). It is also evident in the attempts of certain
religious leaders to subvert education. In answer to the
question " Who Made the World War? " Bishop Thomas
O'Shea told the readers of the *Catholic Digest* in December 1944: " Those who are responsible for modern education are responsible for the present calamity." He suggested that " the best thing we can do in the coming year
is to get rid of our educational leaders and their immoral
creeds and commence a reform of the whole system by
making religion the animating principle of it."

At no time in the history of the world has there been a
greater need for intelligence and special skills. The modern world requires universal education and the expansion

of the frontiers of both the physical and social sciences. It will be difficult enough to promote education and technical competence throughout the world without the obstacles fostered by tradition and superstition in the realms of science, religion, and politics.

10

The Conflict Between
Creeds and Needs

Contemporary refusals to recognize the need for control of the birth rate stem from our early heritage. Primitive man led a precarious life. Because of fluctuating and uncertain sources of food, many people died of hunger or malnutrition. There was no control of disease and little protection against cold and storms. Infant mortality must have been very high, and the average expectancy of life was less than twenty years. The death rate probably exceeded 40 per thousand of population. Under such harsh conditions, a high birth rate was essential for the survival of the human race.

Primitive man's fear and insecurity continue to be reflected in today's irrational demands for large numbers. The ancient fertility cult has become the tool of religion, military needs, and the dogma of racial or religious superiority. With modern death rates, man's inherent fecundity is great enough to double the population every twenty-five years or less. The explosive growth of the world's population within the last three centuries has resulted from decreased death rates unaccompanied by decreased birth rates.

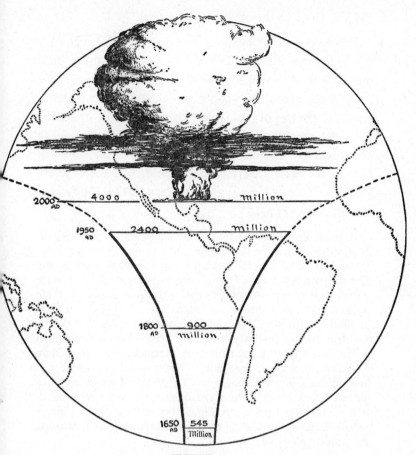

FIGURE 10

THE CHALLENGE OF OVERPOPULATION

The present species of man has lived on this earth for at least 50,000 years and his primitive ancestors for more than 500,000 years. But the world population did not reach 500 million until the sixteenth century A.D. Since 1650 the world population has increased from about 600 million to 2,500 million; at present growth rates it will reach 4,000 million by the year 2000 A.D.

Nearly two-thirds of the world's people live at little above subsistence levels; yet these are the people who have the highest birth rates. The greatest population growth, or potential growth, is in countries that do not now produce adequate food for their present populations. All advances in agriculture and industry could be absorbed by excessive population growth — and the only result of increased production would be more people living in poverty. Poverty and ignorance are greater threats to our modern civilization than the hydrogen bomb.

The most striking evidence of the survival of primitive instincts is the fact that in much of the world today population growth is still controlled by sheer and appallingly high death rates.   A startling — though logical — proposal for control of population growth in these areas has been the suggestion that during the early stages of the Demographic Transition we *permit* rather than *control* high death rates.   Gerald F. Winfield, who spent many years in China as a medical missionary, makes the following proposal (127):

It is obvious that the first objective of the medical-health program must *not* be the simple, natural one of saving lives. Instead, it must be the development of means whereby the Chinese people will reduce their birth rate as rapidly as modern science can reduce the death rate.   The proposition is made with an acute awareness of its radical nature.   For one trained in public health it will seem rank heresy to propose that during the next twenty to thirty years not even severe epidemics in China should be attacked with every means available to modern medicine.   I suggest that public health measures which can save millions of lives should not be practiced in China on a nation-wide scale until the stage is set for a concurrent reduction of the birth rate. . . .   The future welfare of the Chinese people is more dependent on the prevention of births than on the prevention of deaths.

A similar view is expressed by John D. Black (10):

Another point of view is that of the pure unthinking sentimentalist who says that relieving hunger and disease is always good and that it is the moral obligation of other nations to do this just as it is of a doctor to help the sick.   The answer is that, when whole populations are considered, prolonging a few lives this year is of no avail if this causes more misery and suffering in the years following. . . .   Those who speak in this way are charged with being " hard-boiled " and non-humanitarian, but they are the true humanitarians.

Few scientists have dared to face the ethical problems raised by such proposals. However, Sir Arthur V. Hill, president of the British Association for the Advancement of Science, has asked a pertinent question (51): "If ethical principles deny our right to do evil in order that good may come, are we justified in doing good when the foreseeable consequence is evil? " Most people would agree that saving lives and controlling disease is always good. But, Hill continues:

. . . suppose it were certain that the pressure of increasing population, uncontrolled by disease, would lead not only to widespread exhaustion of the soil and of other natural resources, but also to continuing and increasing international tension and disorder, making it hard for civilization to survive, would the majority of humane and responsible people then change their minds?

Temporary and small-scale solutions to excessive population pressures through extensive emigration (Ireland), through an industrialism that permits substantial food imports (England), or through greatly increased food production (Denmark) have encouraged complacent neglect of these general problems. People have therefore been led to the most irrational, tragic consequences.

Hitler, Mussolini, and Tojo claimed that their countries were overpopulated and that their people needed more *Lebensraum*. In the case of Germany the demand was only an excuse for expansion; population growth in Germany was adequately controlled by low birth rates and the country was not subject to excessive population pressure. Italy and Japan were overpopulated and had rapidly growing populations; yet the leaders of these countries never proposed that birth rates be reduced. Instead they demanded higher birth rates to provide larger armies in order to invade and take the land of their neighbors.

A similar proposal was made by the Very Rev. Francis J. Connell in a nationwide radio talk given on September 12, 1954, during " The Catholic Hour." In discussing the " Ethics of War " he stated.

There can be occasions when even a war of conquest will be justifiable, a war waged for the purpose of acquiring more territory. The case would be this: A nation has increased in population to such an extent that there is not sufficient land to provide a decent livelihood for the citizens, so that they are reduced to the direst poverty and starvation. In such circumstances the first duty of the government is to attempt to remedy the situation by peaceful measures, such as purchasing more territory from another nation, or sending some of the people abroad as emigrants who will become loyal and dutiful citizens of the land of their adoption. But it may happen that no other country will sell land, or admit the people of this overcrowded nation into their borders. In that event, when the situation has grown desperate, the nation that is put in this situation of extreme need may lawfully go to war in order to seize a portion of territory that is not needed by another country.*

But who is to decide when " the situation has grown desperate " — and which countries have " a portion of territory that is not needed "? Should the United States welcome millions of immigrants from overpopulated areas each year? If not, should the overcrowded nations of Asia wage war on the relatively sparsely populated countries of North America? Assuming that the people of Asia populated other areas by invasion or by peaceful

* Copies of this talk, " When May a Nation Go to War," may be obtained from the National Council of Catholic Men, 1312 Massachusetts Ave., N.W., Washington 5, D.C.

means, and continued to breed at a prolific rate — what would they do when all of the world became densely populated and all the people were living in poverty? It seems incredible that such an excuse for war could be made by a spokesman of a Christian religion.

Certainly there is no moral reason why the countries that control their birth rates with due regard to national resources should welcome the surplus populations of nations that breed without any consideration of social or economic consequences. If such a policy had been adopted in the past, the entire world population would now be living at subsistence levels.

The attitude toward such ethical considerations is, of course, inevitably bound up with one's religious heritage. It is regrettable that positive traditional values should have become so inflexible as to deny the most obvious possibilities for betterment. Even in the modern Western nations, where the practice of birth control is nearly universal, ancient mores, outmoded attitudes, and legal restrictions limit the general utilization of modern contraceptive techniques. Raymond Pearl, in his 1939 study of the contraceptive practices of 30,000 women in the United States (77), concluded: "What these women, taken as a group, know about contraception is mainly what has been passed on to them by mothers, husbands, friends or drug-store attendants, who in turn derived it from precisely the same kind of sources back to the landing at Ararat." According to Pearl's survey, less than 3 per cent of these women used the modern contraceptive techniques usually recommended by gynecologists, while nearly two-thirds of them relied on primitive methods.

According to Rock and Loth (92), the birth-control method described in the Bible (Genesis 38) is still the greatest single factor in the control of the birth rate.

Traditional prejudices seem to operate with special vigor among Roman Catholics. Catholic opposition to birth control is especially difficult to understand and to combat because it embraces such diverse and conflicting views. Perhaps the most general is the popular blanket prejudice against all types of birth control as simply, and vaguely, immoral. T. R. Hanley, S.J., told a Harvard conference on "Tomorrow's Children" that "no social power and no conceivable set of circumstances can justify birth control" (43). In an address before the Population Association of America on "Catholic Values and the Population Problem," the Rev. W. J. Gibbons expressed the following views (40):

Man needs material wealth, but not at the price of losing his soul. Hence as the Catholic sees it, the morally unacceptable in matters of sex, as well as in other departments of life, cannot be used to solve temporal problems. Ecological difficulties arising from population increase or disequilibrium are no exception.

Even more emphatic is the statement by M. C. Taylor, in discussing the population problems of Puerto Rico: "No stress of poverty, no health reason, no prediction of a doctor, no economic struggle — in a word no reason whatsoever, can render it [artificial birth control] allowable" (108).*

* In Puerto Rico the legislature authorized birth-control clinics; but women were told by the Roman Catholic clergy that contraception is against God's law. As a result, many Puerto Rican women began to demand surgical sterilization — on the ground that sterilization involves only one sin, whereas contraception necessitates continued and frequent sins (99).

Officially, however, the Catholic Church apparently approves of the *principle* of birth control. The following statement in 1938 by the editors of *Fortune* (39) presumably described the official Catholic position:

The controversy between the great Roman Catholic Church and certain non-Catholic groups is not one involving the principle of birth control. Catholic churchmen are on record in many documents as acknowledging the legitimacy of and even the necessity for the control of birth by intelligent means. The quarrel lies not with the end, but with the means. The means permitted by the Catholic Church are based upon what Pope Pius XI referred to (in his Encyclical on *Christian Marriage*, Dec. 31, 1931) as the " circumstances of time " known as the Safe Period method; and to explain how this works, dignitaries of the Church have written or put their imprimatur upon pamphlets and books that are freely distributed through the mails to millions of people. Many of these liberal publications, besides describing the method, have recognized as sound reasons for " family limitation " such factors as unemployment, poverty, worry, and health.

In fact the arguments for the need of birth control presented in one of the most widely distributed " rhythm " books (64) might well have been drawn up by the Planned Parenthood Federation itself.

Finally, there are some who seem to adopt quite irresponsible views. In his pamphlet entitled *Babies, Not Bullets* (originally published as an article in the *Catholic World*), William T. Walsh (122) urges Catholics to " multiply and possess the land." He opposes the " rhythm " method of birth control because " it won't fill the earth with Catholics," and " that is precisely what the world needs."

There is a possibility of satisfying both needs and creeds. When James B. Conant, former president of

Harvard, peered into his " plastic ball " at a meeting of the American Chemical Society (21), he envisaged the development of an oral contraceptive that would be acceptable to religious groups now opposed to the use of mechanical and chemical contraceptives. The basis of Catholic opposition to artificial birth control is clearly defined by William J. Gibbons, S.J.: " By artificial birth control the [Roman Catholic] Church means the use of any mechanical or chemical contraceptives resorted to for the purpose of keeping the male seed from reaching the uterus and thus penetrating to the Fallopian tubes " (40). Obviously the prevention of ovulation could not be classed as " artificial birth control " as defined by Father Gibbons. It is almost certain that a simple, effective, and inexpensive oral contraceptive could be developed and distributed within a few years for less than the cost of a single atomic bomb. An oral contraceptive of this sort would be both a practical solution and perhaps the best possible compromise in regard to the general problem of creeds and needs.

In point of fact there is ample evidence that Catholics practice contraception to about the same extent as non-Catholics of comparable educational economic status. In Massachusetts (where birth control, being " against God's law," is restricted by the laws of the Commonwealth), the average annual birth rate for the years 1936–40 was 14.0 for the seven predominantly Catholic cities (62 per cent Catholic), and 13.9 for the seven predominantly non-Catholic cities (25 per cent Catholic). During the same period the average annual birth rate of Massachusetts was 14.3 — less than France's rate of 14.8. For the

TABLE 13

BIRTH RATES IN CATHOLIC AND NON–CATHOLIC AREAS

Massachusetts city	Catholic population (percentage of total)	Average birth rate (1936–1940)
Salem	68	14.1
Holyoke	65	12.3
Fall River	64	14.5
Lowell	63	14.8
Lawrence	60	13.3
Revere	59	14.3
Fitchburg	57	14.8
Waltham	48	15.5
New Bedford	46	13.4
Pittsfield	46	16.1
Taunton	46	14.6
Worcester	42	14.7
Cambridge	42	16.1
Chelsea	41	14.6
Watertown	40	14.6
Boston	38	14.5
Springfield	38	13.13
Everett	36	17.2
Haverhill	34	12.8
Malden	33	14.8
Lynn	31	13.3
Somerville	30	16.7
Brockton	29	13.5
Arlington	27	13.0
Newton	23	13.6
Brookline	22	9.9
Medford	21	15.6
Quincy	20	14.7
Massachusetts		14.3
United States		17.3
France		14.8
Mexico		43.9

country as a whole, birth rates are lower in the states with large Catholic populations (with the exception of New Mexico which has a large Mexican population) than in the predominantly Protestant states (120). To judge by the results, the great majority of educated Catholics in this country have not accepted the doctrine that " a Catholic who is truly a Catholic must accept the teaching authority of the Catholic Church in the matter of the prevention of conception whether he finds the arguments from reason convincing or not " (40).

Many of the Catholic countries of Europe also have low birth rates. France and Belgium have had birth rates as low as 15 or less, and in recent years Italy's birth rate has dropped below 18 per thousand.

There is no evidence that either religious or political appeals have ever significantly increased the birth rate in any country. Marriage bonuses and baby bonuses in various countries have resulted only in slight and temporary increases in birth rates. In the U.S.S.R. the Communists (as we shall see) are urging a larger population. Yet the Soviet delegates to the International Population Congress, held in Rome in 1954, reported that birth rates in their country had dropped from 38 per thousand (before World War II) to 24 per thousand. It is improbable that either political dogmas or religious taboos can induce educated people to increase birth rates at the expense of at least moderate living standards.

Nevertheless, the fact that certain elements among the Western nations have, or profess to have, scruples as to the use of present-day contraceptives would not greatly matter in such a relatively prosperous and stable demographic group as ours if this were simply a matter of private behavior. The problem is that Catholic opposition constitutes an organized, formidable power, creating serious obstacles to the promotion of any rational birth-control program in the densely populated Catholic and non-Catholic areas of the world. The population problems of these areas, with their great potential growth rates, are generally evaded by the United States Public Health Service, United Nations agencies, and other international organizations — because of Catholic opposition. The failure even to discuss population problems at the F.A.O. Conference on Food and Agriculture was explained by John D. Black as follows: " The reason that birth rates were not discussed at Hot Springs is that they were not deemed a safe subject to talk about in an international meeting. They are tangled up with religion in some countries " (11).

In a pamphlet published in cooperation with UNESCO (73), the authors deny the validity of the Malthusian laws of population growth, and suggest that overpopulation is " hardly more than an evasive name for poverty " — even though the senior author, Alva Myrdal, a distinguished Swedish scientist, is well aware of the problems caused by excessive populations. When a Norwegian delegate suggested that a study of world population problems be undertaken by the World Health Organization of the United Nations, the proposal was immediately vetoed by Catholic delegates, who threatened to boycott the international organization if the suggestion was adopted.

More direct opposition to a birth-control program occurred several years ago in Japan. At the request of

Douglas MacArthur's occupation administration, Edward Ackerman prepared a survey of Japan's resources; in it he advocated control of the birth rate. The Catholic Women's Club of Tokyo, consisting of wives of American occupation forces, protested vigorously — and the report was suppressed. The officer in charge of the Natural Resources Section was reprimanded by General MacArthur for stating that " Japan is a nation of too many people on too little land, and its most serious economic and social problems stem directly from this condition " (22). The Catholic Women's Club also protested when the Birth Control Institute of Tokyo first invited Margaret Sanger to Japan; she was denied an entry permit.

The restrictions imposed upon the World Health Organization are well illustrated by the fate of its birth-control experiment in India. The scope of the program was limited to the " rhythm " method of birth control. Because the great majority of Indians are illiterate and could not use a " rhythm calendar," a simpler method for finding the " safe period " was introduced — appropriately called the " rhythm rosary." After the determination of a woman's menstrual cycle, she was provided with a string of beads of different colors. A standard " rhythm rosary " consisted of 28 beads: 4 pink ones to represent the menstrual period, 4 green beads, 14 red beads, and 6 green beads. The Indian woman was supposed to tick off a bead for each day of the menstrual cycle and observe the " stop " and " go " signs.

As might be expected, the " rhythm " method was not effective. Some of the Indian women refused to use the " rosary " on the ground that " only cows wear that kind of bead." Others were reported as thinking that " merely moving the beads along each day was itself a guarantee against conception." Even when used intelligently, the " rhythm " is not a reliable method of birth control.

In the United States, there are frequent Catholic efforts to discredit the work of the Planned Parenthood Federation and its local agencies. At a recent meeting of the National Catholic Family Life Conference at Columbus, Ohio, the Planned Parenthood Federation was branded as " immoral, un-Christian, subversive " and " destructive of society." Bishop Mussio linked birth control with divorce and free love, and tagged it as " Murder, Incorporated " (93). In several states, doctors have been dismissed from Catholic hospitals for belonging to local planned-parenthood leagues. If a magazine publishes an article favoring birth control, it is deluged with vigorous protests from Catholics (89). In an article prepared for a Boston newspaper at the editor's request, the author stated that the majority of Catholics in Massachusetts practice birth control. The author was requested to delete the statement, with this comment from the editor: " I know that it is true, and the Catholics know that it is true, but if I published such a statement I would have every Catholic in Boston on my neck the next morning."

Positive programs for the dissemination of birth-control information — the main hope we have for a successful Demographic Transition in Asia and other areas — are undermined not only by the Roman Catholic Church but also by Communist Russia. The Communists maintain that, under the Soviet system of economy, ample food and industrial products could be produced for all, regardless of the size of the population. A writer named Kuzminov wrote in an article published in 1951 in *Pravda* (23):

The classics of Marx-Lenin gave a fatal blow to the false theory of Malthus. . . . Poverty, unbearable labor, unemployment, war and other disasters are not an everlasting natural law, but characteristics inherent to the Capitalistic economic system. Engels said that human productivity is beyond measurement and the productivity of the land can be raised infinitely. The great experiences of socialistic construction so far obtained in the Soviet Union completely shut out the vulgar theory of Malthusianism.

In Moscow in 1954, First Secretary Nikita S. Krushchev told a Communist youth organization: " Bourgeois ideologists have invented cannibalistic theories, including the theory of overpopulation. They are thinking about how to reduce the birth rate, how to slow down the growth of population. It is different with us, comrades." He assured the young Russians that, even if another 100 million people were added to the present Russian population of 200 million, " it would be too little. The more people we have, the stronger our country will be."

The Chinese Communists have apparently accepted the party line. An editorial in the *New China News* of September 17, 1949, stated (23):

The fact that China has a vast population is a good thing. Even if her population increased many-fold, she fully has the means to deal with it — the means is production. The absurd theory advanced by the Western bourgeois economists like Malthus that the increase in food cannot keep up with the increase in population has not only been utterly refuted theoretically by

Marxists, but has also been entirely refuted by facts in the post-revolution Soviet Union and liberated areas in China.

But the truth is that yields per acre have increased only about 6 per cent in the U.S.S.R. during the past forty years (17). About 20 per cent more food is produced, largely because of increased acreage; but during the past forty years Russia's population has grown nearly 50 per cent. Agricultural production is not keeping pace with population growth in the U.S.S.R.

China claims a population of over 582 million for 1953 and a growth rate of more than 2 per cent per year. At this rate China's population would approach 1000 million by 1980. China will do well if she can provide adequate food, shelter, clothes, and medical facilities for her present population. According to a report in the *New York Times* of November 10, 1954, some of the Chinese leaders have begun to realize that population growth must be curbed. Shao Li-tze, a deputy of the National People's Congress, declared: " It's a good thing to have a large population, but in an environment beset with difficulties it appears that there should be a limit set." Apparently some of the Chinese Communists have not completely accepted the Marxian doctrine of unlimited population.

It should be evident that the rapid control of the birth rate is essential if there is to be any hope for the Demographic Transition in Asia and other densely populated and underdeveloped areas. When people develop strong motives for birth control and have the knowledge and means to implement these motives, any form of contraceptive is adequate to reduce the birth rate. With low levels of motivation, education, and income, the contraceptives now available are not satisfactory because of psychological barriers, the necessity for some degree of intelligence and foresight in their use, and their exorbitant cost. In order to promote the rapid adoption of birth control in the critical areas of the world it is not enough to increase food supplies, promote local industry, and improve public health and education. These steps are necessary, but at the same time a complete program of birth control must be included in public-health programs. There must be at least as much emphasis on control of the birth rate as on control of the death rate.

We have the knowledge and the potential resources to provide a good life for all of the world's people if population growth can be controlled. But primitive religious taboos and political dogma are serious obstacles to world-wide peace and prosperity. Modern man can choose either a future based on ignorance and superstition, or a future based on science and rational thought. In the future, as in the past, population growth will be controlled by war, famine, and disease — unless birth rates in all parts of the world are soon reduced to moderate levels.

Bibliography

1. Ames, Oakes. *Economic Annuals and Human Cultures.* Cambridge: Botanical Museum, Harvard University, 1939.
2. Ayres, Eugene. " Power from the Sun," *Scientific American,* 1950.
3. Ayres, Eugene, and Scarlott, Charles A. *Energy Sources: The Wealth of the World.* New York: McGraw-Hill, 1952.
4. Baker, O. E. " The Population Prospects in Relation to the World's Agricultural Resources," *Journal of Geography,* 1947.
5. Barr, Stringfellow. *Let's Join the Human Race.* University of Chicago Press, 1950.
6. ———. *Citizens of the World.* New York: Doubleday, 1952.
7. Bateman, Alan M. " Our Future Dependence on Foreign Minerals," *Annals of the American Academy of Political and Social Science,* 1952.
8. Bear, Firman E. " Soil, the Substance of Things Hoped For," *Journal of Soil and Water Conservation,* 1952.
9. Bennett, H. H. " Soil and Water Conservation," *Proceedings of the United Nations Scientific Congress* (New York), 1950.
10. Black, John D. " The Economics of Freedom from Want," *Chronica Botanica,* 1948.
11. ———. " Population and Scarce Food Resources," *Proceedings of the Population Association of America* (Princeton University Press), 1949.

12. Black, John D., and Kiefer, M. E. *Future Food and Agricultural Policy.* New York: McGraw-Hill, 1948.
13. Bradfield, Richard. "Soil Resources and the World's Potential Food Supply," *Proceedings of the Population Association of America* (Princeton University Press), 1949.
14. Brown, Harrison. *The Challenge of Man's Future.* New York: Viking Press, 1954.
15. Burlew, John S. *Algae Culture — From Laboratory to Pilot Plant.* Washington: Carnegie Institution, Publication 600, 1953.
16. Castro, Josue de. *Geography of Hunger.* Boston: Little, Brown, 1952.
17. *Christian Science Monitor,* Dec. 8, 1953.
18. Christman, Ruth E. *Soviet Science.* Washington: American Association for the Advancement of Science, 1952.
19. Clark, F. Le Gros, and Pirie, N. W. *Four Thousand Million Mouths.* London: Oxford University Press, 1951.
20. Clark, G. L. "Dynamics of Production in a Marine Area," *Ecological Monographs,* 1946.
21. Conant, J. B. "A Skeptical Scientist Looks into the Crystal Ball," *Chemical Engineering News,* 1951.
22. Cook, Robert C. *Human Fertility: The Modern Dilemma.* New York: William Sloane Associates, 1951.
23. ———. "Soviet Population Policy," *Population Bulletin* (Washington), 1952.
24. Cressey, G. B. "Land for 2.4 Billion Neighbors," *Economic Geography,* 1953.
25. Curley, Michael J. *Shall We Have Children?* New York: Paulist Press, 1947.
26. Darwin, Charles G. *The Next Million Years.* London: Rupert Hart-Davis, 1952.
27. Davis, D. E. "A Comparison of Reproductive Potential of Two Rat Populations," *Ecology,* 1951.
28. Davis, Kingsley. "The World Demographic Transition," *Annals of the American Academy of Political and Social Science,* 1945.

29. ———. " Population and the Further Spread of Industrial Society," *Proceedings of the American Philosophical Society,* 1951.

30. Dorn, Harold F. " The Effect of Public Health Development upon Population Growth," *Annals of the New York Academy of Science,* 1952.

31. Dublin, L. I. " What It Costs to Raise a Child to 18," *Woman's Home Companion,* May 1947.

32. East, E. M. *Mankind at the Crossroads.* New York: Charles Scribner's Sons, 1923.

33. Eaton, J. W., and Mayer, A. J. " The Social Biology of Very High Fertility Among the Hutterites," *Human Biology,* 1953.

34. Fawcett, Charles B. " The Extent of Cultivable Land," *Geographical Journal,* 1930.

35. ———. " The Numbers and Distribution of Mankind," *Scientific Monthly,* 1947.

36. *Fertilizer Review: 1950 Fertilizer Consumption.* Washington: National Fertilizer Association, 1951.

37. Fischer, John. " India's Insoluble Hunger," *Harper's Magazine,* 1945.

38. Forbes, William H. " What Will India Eat Tomorrow? " *Atlantic Monthly,* 1951.

39. *Fortune* magazine editors. *The Accident of Birth.* New York: Farrar and Rinehart, 1938.

40. Gibbons, William J. " The Catholic Value System in Relation to Human Fertility," *Proceedings of the Population Association of America* (Princeton University Press), 1949.

41. Gill, Tom. *Land Hunger in Mexico.* Washington: Charles Lathrop Pack Forestry Foundation, 1951.

42. Glesinger, Egon. *The Coming Age of Wood.* New York: Simon and Schuster, 1949.

43. Hanley, T. R. " Tomorrow's Children," *Boston American,* July 9, 1942.

44. Hardwicke, R. E. " Adequacy of Our Mineral Fuels," *Annals of the American Academy of Political and Social Science,* 1952.

45. Harris, Seymour E. *Foreign Aid and Our Economy.* Washington: Public Affairs Institute, 1950.

46. Hatt, Paul K. *Backgrounds of Human Fertility in Puerto Rico.* Princeton University Press, 1952.

47. Hatt, Paul K. *World Population and Future Resources.* New York: American Book Company, 1952.

48. Heidt, Lawrence J., and McMillan, A. F. "Conversion of Sunlight into Chemical Energy," *Science,* 1953.

49. Henshaw, Paul S. "Physiologic Control of Fertility," *Science,* 1953.

50. Herrick, G. W. "The Ponderable Substance of Aphids," *Entomological News,* 1926.

51. Hill, Arthur V. "The Ethical Dilemma of Science," *Nature,* 1952.

52. Hottel, Hoyt C. "The Engineering Utilization of Solar Energy," *Proceedings of the American Academy of Arts and Sciences* (Boston), 1951.

53. Hrdlička, A. "Fecundity of Eskimo Women," *American Journal of Physical Anthropology,* 1936.

54. Huxley, Julian. "Population and Human Destiny," *Harper's Magazine,* 1950.

55. Hyland, T. S. "The Fruitful Mountaineers," *Life,* Dec. 26, 1949.

56. Isaacs, R. H. "The Political and Psychological Context of Point Four," *Annals of the American Academy of Political and Social Science,* 1950.

57. Jenkins, Merle. "Genetic Improvement of Food Plants for Increased Yield," *Proceedings of the American Philosophical Society,* 1951.

58. Jeppson, L. R. "Entomological Aspects of Systemic Insecticides," *Journal of Agricultural and Food Chemistry,* 1953.

59. Johnston, Ivan M. "Studies in the Boraginaceae XXIII: A Survey of the Genus Lithospermum," *Journal of the Arnold Arboretum,* 1952.

60. Keenleyside, H. L. "Critical Mineral Shortages," *Proceedings of the United Nations Scientific Conference* (New York), 1950.

61. Kellogg, C. E. *Food, Soil and People.* New York: UNESCO (Manhattan Publishing Company), 1950.

62. *Ladies Home Journal,* March 1938.

63. Lamb, George A. "The Fuel Complex: A Projection," *Annals of the American Academy of Political and Social Science,* 1952.

64. Latz, Leo J. *The Rhythm.* Chicago: Latz Foundation, 1939.

65. León, Alberto, and Aldama, A. C. "Population Problems in Central and Caribbean America," *Annals of the American Academy of Political and Social Science,* 1945.

66. Levorsen, A. I. "Estimates of Undiscovered Petroleum Reserves," *Proceedings of United Nations Scientific Conference,* Vol. 1, 1950.

67. McCabe, L. C. *World Resources and Consumption of Energy: Energy in the Service of Man.* New York: United Nations, 1951.

68. McNevin, W. C. "The Trapping of Solar Energy," *Ohio Journal of Science,* 1953.

69. Malthus, T. R. *An Essay on the Principle of Population,* Vol. 1. First American edition, third London edition, 1809.

70. Mather, Kirtley F. *Enough and to Spare.* New York: Harper and Brothers, 1944.

71. Metropolitan Life Insurance Company. "Longevity from Ancient to Modern Times," *Statistical Bulletin* (New York), 1947.

72. Murphy, W. J. "Nonpharmaceutical Uses of Antibiotics," *Journal of Agricultural and Food Chemistry,* 1953.

73. Myrdal, Alva, and Vincent, Paul. *Are There Too Many People?* New York: UNESCO (Manhattan Publishing Company), 1950.

74. Notestein, Frank W. "Problems of Policy in Relation to Areas of Heavy Population Pressure," in *Demographic Studies of Selected Areas of Rapid Growth.* New York: Milbank Memorial Fund, 1944.

75. Osborn, Fairfield. *Our Plundered Planet.* Boston: Little, Brown, 1948.

76. Paley, William S. *Resources for Freedom,* IV. Washington: President's Material Policy Commission, 1952.

77. Pearl, Raymond. *Natural History of Population.* New York: Oxford University Press, 1939.

78. Pearson, Frank A., and Harper, F. A. *The World's Hunger.* Ithaca, N.Y.: Cornell University Press, 1945.

79. Pehrson, E. W. "Estimates of Selected World Mineral Supplies," *Proceedings of the United Nations Scientific Conference* (New York), 1950.

80. Pendell, Elmer. *Population on the Loose.* New York: Wilfred Funk, 1951.

81. Pincus, G. *The Mammalian Egg.* New York: Macmillan, 1936.

82. Piquet, Howard S. "Point Four and World Production," *Annals of the American Academy of Political and Social Science,* 1950.

83. *Population Index.* Princeton: Office of Population Research, Princeton University. Published quarterly.

84. Prentice, E. Parmalee. *Food, War and the Future.* New York: Harper and Brothers, 1944.

84b. Putnam, P. C. *Energy in the Future.* New York: Van Nostrand, 1953.

85. Quisenberry, K. S. "Crop Production Potentials in Relation to Freedom from Want," *Chronica Botanica,* 1948.

86. Rabinowitch, E. "The World's Energy Supplies and Their Utilization," *Proceedings of the American Academy of Arts and Sciences* (Boston), 1951.

87. Raushenbush, S. "Economic Considerations in Conservation and Development," *Proceedings of the United Nations Scientific Conference* (New York), 1950.

88. ———. *People, Food, Machines.* Washington: Public Affairs Institute, 1950.

89. *Reader's Digest.* "The Catholic Case Against Margaret Sanger," *Reader's Digest,* Dec. 1951.

90. Reed, S. C. "The Disintegration of Civilization," *Journal of Heredity,* 1949.

91. Rock, John. "Medical and Biological Aspects of Contraception," *Clinics,* 1943.

92. Rock, John, and Loth, David. *Voluntary Parenthood.* New York: Random House, 1949.

93. Rogers, Herbert. "A Roman Catholic Dilemma," *The Churchman*, April 1952.

94. Rosin, Jacob, and Eastman, Max. *The Road to Abundance.* New York: McGraw-Hill, 1953.

95. Russell, Bertrand. *New Hopes for a Changing World.* New York: Simon and Schuster, 1951.

96. Salaman, R. N. *The History and Social Influence of the Potato.* London: Cambridge University Press, 1949.

97. Salter, Robert M. "World Soil and Fertilizer Resources in Relation to Food Needs," *Chronica Botanica,* 1948.

98. Sanger, Margaret. *The Pivot of Civilization.* New York: Brentano's, 1922.

99. Senior, Clarence. "An Approach to Research in Overcoming Cultural Barriers to Family Limitation," *Proceedings of the Population Association of America* (Princeton University Press), 1949.

100. Sheldon, W. H.; Hartl, E. M.; and McDermott, E. *Varieties of Delinquent Youth.* New York: Harper and Brothers, 1949.

101. Sherman, H. C. and Campbell, H. L. "Growth and Reproduction upon Simplified Food Supply," *Journal of Biological Chemistry,* 1924.

102. Shurr, S. H. "The Economics of Atomic Power," *Scientific American,* 1951.

103. Slonaker, J. R. "The Effect of Different Per Cents of Protein in the Diet," *American Journal of Physiology,* 1931.

104. Slonaker, J. R., and Card, T. A. "The Effect of Restricted Diet," *American Journal of Physiology,* 1923.

105. Spengler, J. J. "Economic Factors in the Development of Densely Populated Areas," *Proceedings of the American Philosophical Society,* 1951.

106. Spoehr, H. A. "Chlorella as a Source of Food," *Proceedings of the American Philosophical Society,* 1951.

107. Stamp, L. Dudley. *Land for Tomorrow.* Bloomington: Indiana University Press, 1952.

108. Taylor, M. C. "Neo-Malthusianism in Puerto Rico," *Review of Social Economics,* 1952.

109. Thaysen, A. C. "Food Yeast in the British Empire," *Proceedings of the United Nations Scientific Conference* (New York), 1950.

110. Thompson, Warren S. *Plenty of People.* New York: Ronald Press, 1948.

111. Thompson, Warren S. "Population as a World Problem," *Annals of the New York Academy of Science,* 1952.

112. Treuber, Irene B., and Beal, Edwin G. "The Demographic Heritage of the Japanese Empire," *Annals of the American Academy of Political and Social Science,* 1945.

113. United Nations. *Food and Agriculture: World Conditions and Prospects.* Washington: Food and Agriculture Organization, 1949.

114. United Nations. *Population Bulletin,* No. 1. New York: United Nations, 1951.

115. United Nations. *Preliminary Report on the World Social Situation.* New York, 1952.

116. United States Department of Agriculture. *Agricultural Outlook Charts.* Washington, 1950.

117. United States Department of State. *World Population Estimates.* Office of Intelligence Research, Report 4192. Washington, 1947.

118. United States Department of State. *Energy Resources of the World.* Publication 3428. Washington, 1949.

119. United States Department of State. *Point Four.* Washington, pub. 3719, 1950.

120. United States Census. *Census of Religious Bodies 1936: Statistical Abstracts of the United States.* Washington: U.S. Bureau of Census, 1943.

121. Vogt, William. *Road to Survival.* New York: William Sloane Associates, 1948.

122. Walsh, William T. *Babies, Not Bullets.* New York: Paulist Press, 1939.

123. Waugh, L. M. "A Study of the Nutrition and Teeth of the Eskimos," *Journal of Dental Research,* 1930.

124. Webb, Walter Prescott. "Ended: Four Hundred Year Boom," *Harper's Magazine,* 1951.

125. Weiss, F. J. "Food from the Sea," *Journal of Agricultural and Food Chemistry*, 1953.

126. Wiesner, B. P., and Judkin, John. "Inhibition of Oestrus by Cultivated Gromwell," *Nature*, 1952.

127. Winfield, Gerald F. *China, the Land and the People*. New York: William Sloane Associates, 1948.

128. Woytinsky, W. S., and Woytinsky, E. S. *World Population and Production*. New York: Twentieth Century Fund, 1953.

129. Zimmermann, Erich W. *World Resources and Industries*. New York: Harper and Brothers, 1951.

130. Zirkle, Conway. *The Death of a Science in Russia*. Philadelphia: University of Pennsylvania Press, 1949.

Index

Ackerman, Edward: survey of Japan's resources, 188

Africa: agriculture, 136; coal reserves, 92; demographic status, 24, 40; energy consumption, 88; population, 28, 40; water power, 97

Agriculture: advances in, 105–107; and cultivated land of world, 80–81; early development of, 31–32, 66–67; as foundation of civilization, 78; percentage of workers in, 69; techniques of, 77–78; tropical, 82–83; in U.S.S.R., 191

Algae: for food, 110–112, 116; marine, 84–85

Animals: energy produced by, 87; and human diets, 64; reproductive rates of, 13–15

Antibiotics: and disease, 49; as growth stimulants, 105

Asia: agriculture, 38, 69; coal reserves, 91; demographic status, 24; dietary standards, 64; energy consumption, 88; future prospects, 138–146; petroleum reserves, 95; population, 37; water power, 97

Atomic energy: reserves, 113; utilization, 114

Automobiles: energy output of, 88; world distribution of, 128

Ayres, Eugene: on nuclear fusion, 114; on solar energy, 115

Barr, Stringfellow: on cost of war, 156

Bateman, Alan M.: on U.S. mineral imports, 101

Bear, Firman: on U.S. food production, 77–78

Bennett, H. H.: on soil erosion, 76

Birth control: methods of, 121, 188–189; motives for, 50–51, 148. *See also* Contraceptives

— practice of: in Ireland, 48; in Japan, 146; in Massachusetts, 185; in U.S., 181; in U.S.S.R., 190

— opinion of: as murder, 189; as cannibalistic, 190

Birth rates: and diets, 165; causes of decline of, 161–167; differential, 169; in various countries, 128

Black, John D.: on death rates, 178; on food resources, 84

Boyd-Orr, Sir John, 163

Catholic: birth rates, 184–185; definition of "artificial" birth control, 184; opposition to birth control, 7, 180, 186–189

Central America: demographic status, 24; population growth, 137; resources, 136

Ceylon: death rates, 134; population growth, 134

China: agriculture, 139; arable land, 140; farms, 189; food needs, 140; population, 138; population growth, 191; views on birth control, 190

Chlorella, 110

Clark, G. L.: on marine conversion cycle, 85

Coal: distribution, 92; reserves, 93, 95; world consumption, 92

Colonial empires: and Demographic Transition, 43, 48
Communists: and birth control, 8, 190
Connecticut: potential population growth in, 38
Connell, Rev. Francis J.: on overpopulation as excuse for war, 180
Contraceptives: ancient, 182; physiological, 121–122, 173; in U.S., 181
Cook, Robert C.: on biological illiterates, 149; on population of English descent, 54
Crop plants: hybrid corn as, 70; new varieties of, 69–70; yields of, 71–72

Darwin, Charles: influence of Malthus on, 17
Darwin, Sir Charles G.: on modern civilization, 168
Davis, Kingsley: on Asian birth rates, 128
Death rates: control of, 49; due to famine and malnutrition, 39, 47; in various countries, 19, 24; primitive, 33–34
De Castro, J.: on diet and fertility, 162–166
Demographic status of world, 23–27, 128
Demographic Transition: definition of, 4; of western Europe, North America, and Oceania, 42, 58–59, 104
— prospects for: in Asia, 138–144; in Africa, 136; in Central America, 136–138; in eastern and southern Europe, 130–131; in South America, 134–135; in U.S.S.R., 131
Dublin, L. I.: on cost of raising children, 50

Economics: agricultural, 78, 84; and birth rates, 158; of industrialization, 158–160; and status of areas of world, 128
Emigration: from England, 55; from Europe, 46; from Ireland, 47; from Italy, 46; prospects for, from India, 143
Energy: atomic, 113–114; from draft animals, 87; from fossil fuel, 92; from man, 87; from water power, 97; solar, 115–119; world consumption of, 88–90
England: death rates, 33; Demographic Transition, 53–55, 59; food imports, 12; population growth, 12, 55
Eugenics, 169–170
Europe: agriculture, 76; coal resources, 92; demographic status, 24; Demographic Transition, 43; energy consumption, 88; water-power resources, 97

Fertilizers: organic, 32, 66; mineral, 68; use of, in various parts of world, 68
Fish: potential reproduction of, 14; production and resources, 85
Fisher and Burlew: on algae culture, 112
Food: and birth rates, 164; composition of, 64; consumption of, 62; imports of, 45; production of, 71–72; requirements of, 65, 72
— new sources of: algae as, 110–112; synthetic, 107–108; wood as, 108
Food and Agriculture Organization: estimates of world's arable land, 73; nutritional standards, 62
Forbes, W. H.: on problems of industry in India, 141
Forests: of world, 108; of South America, 135
France: Demographic Transition, 56

French Canadians: population growth of, 15, 56

Fuel: algae as, 116; coal as, 93; petroleum as, 95, wood as, 108

Fungicides, 68

Furnas, C. C.: on energy needs, 98

Gibbons, Rev. W. J.: view of population problem, 182; view of artificial birth control, 184

Glesinger, Egon: on wood for fuel and food, 108

Greece: early death rates, 29; early history of soil erosion, 67

Hager, Floyd: on reproduction of Orchids, 14

Harris, Seymour: on industrial development, 158–159

Heidt, L. J.: on conversion of solar energy, 119

Henshaw, Paul: on oral contraceptives, 121

Herrick, G. W.: on reproduction of aphids, 13

Hill, Sir Arthur: on ethics of controlled death rates, 179

Hu Shih: on material and spiritual values, 157

Hutterites: population growth of, 16

Huxley, Julian: on early population growth, 31

Hybrid vigor, 57, 70

Hydrogen: conversion of, 114

India: agriculture, 140; birth control, 188–189; dietary standards, 140; famine, 39; industrialization, 141–143; population growth, 142; relief from population pressure by emigration, 143–144

Industrialization: and birth rates, 140–142; energy used by, 88; in Europe, 45; in underdeveloped areas, 134–143

Insecticides, 107

Ireland: emigration, 47; population decline, 47–48; potato famine, 47

Italy: birth rates, 186; emigration, 47; population growth, 47

Japan: agriculture, 133; birth rates, 132, 146; population growth, 132

Jenkins, Merle: on yields of hybrid corn, 57

Keith, Sir Arthur: on early world population, 30

Koya, Y.: birth-control program in Japan, 146

Land: arable, 73, 81; cultivated, 80–81; tropical, 83–84

Latin America: demographic status, 24, 50; energy consumption, 88; resources, 92, 97; population growth, 28, 36

Levorsen, A. I.: estimates of petroleum reserves, 94

Life expectancy: in Bronze and Iron age, 33; in England, 33, 34; in Asia, 39. *See also* Death rates

Lithospermum: distribution of, 121; as oral contraceptive, 121

Little, Arthur D., Company, 111

Machines, farm, 69, 89

Malthus, T. H.: laws of population growth, 11–13, 21; on positive checks, 16, 19; on preventive checks, 18–19

— views of, opposed by: Catholics, 21; Communists, 21–22; scientists, 22–23

Man: energy output of, 87; reproductive capacity of, 15

Massachusetts: low birth rates in Catholic cities, 185; restrictions on birth control, 185

Mather, Kirtley: on declining birth rates, 161; estimates of world resources, 3; views on Malthusian laws, 22

Medicine: effect of, on life expectancy, 34; need for, in China, 39
Mexico: agriculture, 137; population problems, 153–54
Minerals: needed in industry, 99; reserves of, 100; U.S. imports of, 101
Myrdal, Alva: views on Malthusian laws, 23, 187

Nehru, J.: and population policy in India, 172
North America: coal reserves, 95; demographic status, 24; dietary standards, 64; energy consumption, 88; water-power consumption, 96
Notestein, Frank W.: on demographic areas, 23; on emigration, 144

Oceania: demographic status, 24; population growth, 28
Oceans: as source of food, 85

Peace: and population pressure, 13; tithe for, 157
Pearl, Raymond: on birth control, 181
Pehrson, E. W.: on mineral resources, 100; on petroleum reserves, 95
Pendleton, Robert: on productivity of tropical soils, 83
Petroleum: consumption of, 94; distribution of, 95; reserves of, 94–95
Pitt, William: influenced by Malthus, 12
Plant: conversion of solar energy, 117; rate of reproduction, 14
Point Four: need for, 150; objectives of, 155; and world economic status, 128
Population: of continental areas, 28; growth of, 20, 28, 34–35, 177; need for control of, 5, 38;

policies of Hitler, Mussolini, and Tojo, 179–180
Puerto Rico: conflict between creeds and needs, 182; population growth, 148–149
Putnam, P. C.: on coal reserves, 93

Quisenberry, K. S.: on new crop varieties, 69–70

Raushenbush, S.: projection of world rehabilitation costs, 155; reluctance to alter tradition, 171
Reed, S. C.: on differential birth rates, 169
Religion: and birth control, 5, 7, 20. See also Catholic
Resources, material, 61. See also Coal; Land; Minerals; Petroleum; Water
Rhythm method, 183–188
Rock, John: on low birth rates, 167, 182
Rockefeller Foundation: and projects in Mexico, 152–153
Rosin, Jacob: on food production, 107; on mineral reserves, 102
Russell, Bertrand: on sex superstitions, 172

Salaman, R. N.: on potato famine in Ireland, 47
Salter, R. M.: estimates of world's arable land, 75, 83
Sanger, Margaret: on communist views of birth control, 21
Soil: conditioners, 106; conservation, 76; erosion, 67; fertility, 66. See also Fertilizers
Solar energy: contributions of, to present resources, 117; magnitude of, 117; new techniques for conversion of, 118–119
South America: demographic status, 24; forests, 135; population, 40; water power, 97
Spoehr, H. A.: on algae for food, 110

Stamp, L. Dudley: on land use in tropics, 83

Sweden: Demographic Transition, 54; differential birth rates, 170

Thompson, Warren: on demographic areas, 23; on urban life and sterility, 167

Tractors: energy output of, 89; world distribution of, 89

Transportation, development of, 20

Treuber, Irene: on demographic needs of Asia, 160; on demographic trends in Japan, 160

Truman, H. S.: and needs for world rehabilitation, 150

United Fruit Company: educational program in Latin America, 151

United States: agricultural production, 72, 74; meat consumption and human fertility, 166; population growth, 58

— reserves: of coal, 92; of minerals, 101; of petroleum, 95

U.S.S.R.: agriculture, 131, 191; birth rates, 186; demographic status, 24; use of energy, 88; population growth, 28; opposition to birth control, 8, 190

— reserves: of coal, 92; of petroleum, 95

Vogt, William: on family size in Sweden, 170; on land in Mexico, 138

War: cost of modern, 156; and destruction of civilization, 156

Water: present utilization for power, 96–97; resources of world, 96–97

Webb, Walter Prescott: on limits of land frontiers, 57

Winfield, Gerald W.: on Chinese birth rates, 178; on Chinese death rates, 39

Wood: as source of food and energy, 108

Yeast: as food, 109